FULL CIRCLE
Recovery

Your guide to feeding the body, mind, and spirit.

Andrea ~
Honored to walk this
road alongside such a
beautiful woman. May
you have peace, love,
happiness, and good
health for the
rest of your
years.
Susanne
11-10-21

To contact the publisher, visit www.kdp.amazon.com

To contact the Author: fullcirclerecovery@hotmail.com

Adriana Quintero
        Cover design
Ernie Sanchez
        Format & content design
Amy Pattee Colvin
        Editorial assessment & book launching services

ISBN: 978-0-578-91611-8

Printed in the United States of America

DEDICATION

*To the men and women
who suffer from addiction,
may you find solace in your journey
of recovery and be well.*

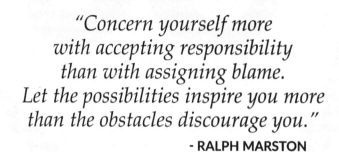

*"Concern yourself more
with accepting responsibility
than with assigning blame.
Let the possibilities inspire you more
than the obstacles discourage you."*

- RALPH MARSTON

DISCLAIMER

The content of this book is for general informational purposes only. It is not meant to be used, nor should it be used, to diagnose or treat any medical condition or to replace the services of your physician or another healthcare provider. The advice and strategies contained in the book may not be suitable for all readers. Please consult your healthcare provider for any questions that you may have about your medical situation. Neither the author, publisher, editor, nor any of their employees or representatives guarantees the accuracy of the information in this book or its usefulness to a particular reader, nor are they responsible for any damage or negative consequence that may result from any treatment, action taken, or inaction by any person reading or following the information in this book.

This book was created to provide information about natural remedies and cures used in the past. This information is made available with the knowledge that the publisher, editor, and author do not offer legal or otherwise medical advice. Therefore, if you are ill, you should always consult with your caring physician or another medical specialist.

This book does not claim to contain and indeed does not contain all the information available on natural remedies for addiction.

While the author has gone to great lengths to provide the most valuable and accurate collection of healing remedies, there may still exist typographical and content errors.

Therefore, this book is not a medical guide.

The author, editor, and publisher shall incur no liability or be held responsible to any person or entity regarding loss of life or injury, alleged or otherwise, that happened directly or indirectly due to using the information contained in this book. Therefore, it is your responsibility, and if you want to use a plant, herb, tea, tincture, or anything else referenced from this book, you should consult with your physician first.

The author and editor of this book made no guarantees of any kind, expressed or implied, regarding the final results obtained by applying the information found in this book. Therefore, making, using, and consuming any of the products described will be done at your own risk.

By reading past this point, you hereby agree to be bound to this disclaimer.

*"When I started counting my blessings,
my whole life turned around."*

- WILLIE NELSON

ACKNOWLEDGEMENTS

Writing this book has been a great joy. Many aspects have been instrumental in my journey of whole health. I have tried to include all of those aspects in this book; certainly, some have been missed.

I am grateful for the many friends and family that have touched my life thus far; there are far too many to list. Please forgive me for not personally mentioning each one of you.

I am immensely grateful for my supportive husband, Tim, and my beautiful daughter Samantha. You both have tolerated and loved me through the years. I do realize this has not been an easy task. Thank you for all that you have taught me, much of which you may never know.

Jill Johnston, my dear friend and fearless leader. You have shared your wisdom to guide and mold me into the woman I am today. Through your experience, strength, and hope, you have shown me how to live freely and beyond my wildest dreams.

Kelly McAvoy, you are a gem! Thank you for generously enhancing the text for my readers, your meticulous editing skills, and the endless hours you graciously poured into my project. You indeed are a gift. Your input has been priceless!

Amy Deakins, I am grateful for the friendship we have acquired throughout the years. You have been my greatest cheerleader and kept me going on those days I wanted to give up. You have brought so much insight and inspiration to my life through your incredible wisdom.

Erin Meadows, I feel blessed to have connected with such a patient accountability partner. Your gentle approach brought forth kept me moving along, week by week, to the finish line.

Elaine Gordon, I cannot thank you enough. Using your expertise to coach me in building Sweet Cakes, you lead me to a life-changing education of holistic nutrition. With this well-rounded knowledge received from the Institute for Integrative Nutrition, my mind opened to many possibilities that ultimately led to writing this book and to a "Full Circle Recovery."

Most of all, I am grateful for the strength I find through God. He has brought forth encouragement through the people who have entered my life on this fantastic journey.

ACKNOWLEDGEMENTS

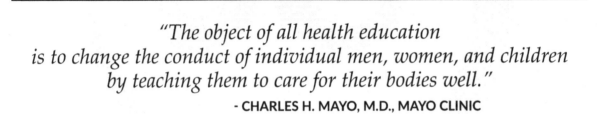

*"The object of all health education
is to change the conduct of individual men, women, and children
by teaching them to care for their bodies well."*

- CHARLES H. MAYO, M.D., MAYO CLINIC

CONTENTS

*"You can't just sit there and
wait for people to give you that golden dream;
you've got to get out there
and make it happen for yourself."*

- DIANA ROSS

INTRODUCTION
My Experience, Strength, and Hope

I was newly sober, and life was good. With the support of my husband and sweet little girl, I opened a retail bakery. I looked forward to getting up and going to work, loved my customers, and felt lucky to have dependable employees by my side. There was always something exhilarating happening on Park Lane, where my thriving little business was nestled in the center of our touristy little hometown. The bakery was part of the charm at this destination, and I happily spent many hours there day in and day out. For many years, joy and contentment filled my heart.

Then slowly, I reached a turning point. It started with a deep sense of misalignment; something did not feel right. I tried to brush it off, but the feeling remained persistent. Finally, thanks to a willingness to pick up the tools acquired from working a recovery program in Alcoholics Anonymous, I was ready to pinpoint the nagging feelings. It became crystal clear that my work-life balance was not as balanced or content as I thought. In all actuality, my life was falling apart. In a significant way, I no longer believed in the products that my business produced. I had been well aware that sugar was harmful to the human body and our wellbeing, and I increasingly became physically sick from overindulgence of sugary processed treats and copious amounts of caffeine. Worn out from the fast pace that a small business often demands, it became evident that this pace of life was taking a toll on my physical health. In hindsight, my diet was a reflection of my lifestyle. Burnout was my final destination. Clearly, I needed to make a change, so I began to take the necessary steps.

Thanks to my proactive approach to life and the support from others, I took a leap of faith and made the necessary changes. First, I sold the little bakery that I loved and adored, and then I earned a holistic, integrative nutrition certificate. This is where my life took a significant and positive shift. I will never forget that first day, as I listened to the nutrition course outlined by founder Joshua Rosenthal. I learned how profoundly lifestyle and nutrition affect the human body, mind, and spirit. This approach fully lined up with living the sober life I had acquired. That feeling of comfort and peace rose within me, similar to returning home after a long journey. I cried tears of joy.

I quickly embraced these concepts and applied them to myself. Within months, debilitating IBS symptoms subsided, and brain fog vanished. Chronic symptoms of arthritis have disappeared, and my joint pains are almost nonexistent. Instead of masking symptoms, I have gained the ability to tune in to my intuition which guides me to a greater awareness of my addictive behaviors, allowing me to take action before real damage can take hold. The knowledge gained was so much more than simply adhering to proper nutrition; it is astonishing just how brilliant the human body is. Our bodies can heal and even avoid so many diseases that we face in today's world. With proper nutrition and fundamental lifestyle changes, we can virtually be drug-free, given half the chance!

Armed with my newfound knowledge of nutrition and lifestyle ideas, I wanted to find ways to educate others and spread this message of health and hope. I coach clients one-on-one, guiding, mentoring, and empowering them to take responsibility for their health. I launched a healthy food product, taught online detox courses, and performed cooking demonstrations. I also designed and implemented a wellness program for a recovery center, teaching what I had learned. All these experiences led to writing *Full Circle Recovery*.

My passionate goal is to support my fellow recovering alcoholics with their health and wellness struggles using a holistic approach. I have brought together simple steps, tips, and techniques that I have used personally and gathered them into one source. I hope you will discover that simply feeding your body proper nutrition, making some essential lifestyle changes, and being rigorously honest throughout this process can profoundly impact your health and sobriety.

In modern society, we are bombarded with conflicting information daily on how to live a healthy life. As a result, we often overcomplicate, leaving us feeling frustrated, confused, and overwhelmed, frequently resulting in a quick fix, relying on prescription drugs to mask the root cause of ailments with dangerous side effects. I have chosen the holistic path, free of all pharmaceuticals and mind-altering substances, and I have never regretted it! My message is to keep it simple. As a woman active in recovery, I have learned to trust my intuition and focus on my guidance from my higher power, which I call God. I encourage you to explore your intuition, awareness, and connection to your higher power.

Finding personal support, whether working with a sponsor, a support group, or a professional, is the stepping stone to implementing and sustaining lifestyle and behavioral changes that will contribute to achieving your personal wellness goals.

With the shift away from old patterns, change is possible. I have acquired many rewarding years of a healthy life I love. I believe if you are willing to work for it, this is also obtainable for you!

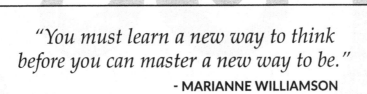

*"You must learn a new way to think
before you can master a new way to be."*

- MARIANNE WILLIAMSON

HOW TO USE THIS BOOK

FOLLOW THESE SIMPLE INSTRUCTIONS

Making simple changes does not have to be complicated, but it does take consistent action. This book will help guide you to doing just that. Along the way, you may find yourself distracted by details or tempted to overcomplicate things. Relax and stay focused. Follow these simple instructions, and you will experience success, one day at a time.

MAKE IT YOUR OWN

Just as no one diet is suitable for everyone, there is no one best plan for everyone. The information in this book reflects on years of experience helping others build successful changes. Although not every suggestion will be right for you, learn to use your intuition, resources, and intelligence to personalize your strategy.

GET SUPPORT

Enlist your family and friends to cheer you on or hire experts to advise on their fields. Having a support team dramatically increases your chances of success.

DO THE EXERCISES AND
CREATE AN ACTION PLAN

There are intentionally open spaces left for notes throughout this workbook, so please make a mess of it. Then, when in doubt, reach out to a support member, refer to your notes, and create an action plan to keep you on track.

GO AT YOUR OWN PACE
(BUT DON'T PROCRASTINATE)

This book contains a lot of information; you do not have to do everything at once. Success is the tiny changes that make a significant impact. Some steps will be easy and fun. Others will be challenging. The vital insight offered is merely head knowledge; information alone changes nothing, consistent action is necessary to make measurable change.

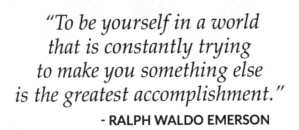

"To be yourself in a world
that is constantly trying
to make you something else
is the greatest accomplishment."
- RALPH WALDO EMERSON

BIO-INDIVIDUALITY

In 1956, Roger Williams published Biochemical Individuality, asserting that individuality permeates each part of the human body. His book explained how personal differences in anatomy, metabolism, compositions of bodily fluids, and cell structure influence your overall health. Each person, Williams wrote, has genetically determined and highly individualistic nutrition requirements. This theory influenced some independent thinking minds in the nutrition world but is still largely ignored by mainstream medicine.

Watching fad diets over the years, from high-carbs in the '70s, low fat in the '80s, to high protein and high fat in the 21st century, it is a wonder how each nutrition expert can claim their diets work for everyone. We are too individualistic to eat the same food. If you notice, men, women, children, teens, and adults have vastly different dietary needs. People who work more sedentary than those who do physical labor, whether 25, 55, or older, have different needs. Ancestry is also a significant factor in shaping Bio-Individuality.

Scientific research is starting to catch on to this concept. In a 2008 study, scientists found that men and women do eat differently. *FoodNet* looked at the eating habits of more than 14,000 American adults and found that generally, men are more likely to report eating meat and poultry, and women are more likely to report eating more fruits and vegetables.

A November 2015 study published in *Cell* found that universal dietary recommendations do not work. Instead, researchers wanted to understand which foods cause people's blood sugar levels to spike, so they measured 800 people over a week, measuring over 46,000 meals. They found that, surprisingly, each person had different glucose responses to similar foods. For example, many people in the study had a low glucose response to ice cream, a sugary food that should spike glucose levels. That research canceled traditional ideas of good and bad foods and that anyone specific diet would work for everyone.

Our tastes and preferences, shapes and sizes, gut bacterial profile, metabolic rates, and genetic backgrounds influence which foods will and will not nourish us. It is too much of a generalization when experts say, "red meat is unhealthy" or "tomatoes are good for us." **One person's food is another person's poison.** Fad diets do not work in the long run; in reality we all have different dietary needs.

*"We are the sum of our actions,
and therefore our habits
make all the difference."*

- ARISTOTLE

THE 90/10 DIET THEORY

While studying at the Institute for Integrative Nutrition (IIN), I was introduced to the 90-10 diet theory, inspired by Joshua Rosenthal. The rule is that 90% of the time, you eat what is healthy for you, and 10% of the time, you eat whatever you feel like eating.

If you notice that when people try to eat a totally clean and pure diet, they can only do it for a limited amount of time. Sometimes it is a day, a week, a month, or even a year. At a certain point, no matter how strong your determination might be, certain foods that you are avoiding become increasingly appealing. This realization inspired Joshua to create his dietary theory, which I have incorporated in my own life with overwhelming success.

Countless people try to stay 100% on their chosen diet program, which is bound to cause stress and likely to fail. So why turn dietary mistakes into sins? Possessing fear and guilt around food is not healthy. Cravings are an opportunity to listen to the body and fine-tune nutritional habits. By giving yourself a 10% range of flexibility, you can indulge yourself without guilt and maintain a healthy diet.

Balance simply means letting loose occasionally, so you do not feel restricted. The point of wellness is not to adhere to anything so strictly that you miss out on all the joy of life.

From the beginning of my sobriety, I have attended numerous AA meetings, spiritual retreats, and I have repeatedly worked the suggested *Twelve Steps of Alcoholics Anonymous* to the best of my ability. I have heard countless recovering alcoholics and addicts' struggles and the issues they continue to face in recovery. However, there is one commonality with stories I have listened to that has stood out to me over the years. After getting clean and sober from drugs and alcohol, many people in recovery trade one addiction for another, replacing it with substances such as sugar, caffeine, energy drinks, or processed junk foods. In addition, addicts seemingly find other ways to fill voids, feel good, or numb out and avoid underlying conditions, consciously or subconsciously. Often, these behaviors lead to different life or health consequences and a continuation with difficulty finding their true self and reaching the potential of living a healthy, sober lifestyle. Frequently this leads to additional health problems and a grueling path of multiple doctors' visits, prescription medicines, and unnecessary surgeries.

If you are serious about creating a healthy lifestyle and doing the work necessary to promote change, this book is for you. This workbook is a tool to guide you in building your roadmap. My intent is simple-to supply you with easy-to-implement ideas and help you set small achievable goals and become the best and healthiest self you deserve to be in this lifetime.
The information provided in this workbook is not a replacement for your drug and prescribed recovery treatment; instead, it is a beneficial compliment!

Before you begin this journey, I encourage you to set aside everything you think you know about yourself, to have an open mind, and allow yourself to have a new experience achieving your personal wellness goals.

*"Let food be thy medicine
and medicine be thy food."*

- HIPPOCRATES

CHAPTER 1:
EATING FOR RECOVERY

Most of us would love to be more energetic and healthier, yet we make excuses that our busy lives deny us the time and energy to accomplish this. The good news is it is possible to obtain these goals without making radical changes.

So, how can we apply successful nutritional changes to our own life? In this workbook, we will go over practical tips to make lasting changes; some may be familiar, and some may be new ideas. With food such a controversial topic, I urge you to have an open mind as you proceed through these pages. Take what you like and leave the rest. Bio-Individuality is a concept so often overlooked; I invite you to explore it for yourself. Do some personal experimentation and find what works best for you at this stage of your life.

Detoxification maintains good health and is vital to maximize the body's energy, preventing chronic illnesses. Although toxins are present everywhere, you can reduce the effects by using the methods suggested. It is normal to have small amounts of toxins in the body, I hope you will see how your choices can help you reach your best and healthiest self. It really can be as simple as adding in more of the good foods that nourish you and crowding out the ones that do not.

Dietary changes are crucial to persons in recovery from addiction to alcohol and drugs.

All alcoholics are malnourished to some extent because excessive alcohol interferes with the body's ability to absorb and use various nutrients regardless of what the alcoholic may be eating. The cells are dependent on an adequate supply of nutrients to perform their everyday functions, heal themselves, and create new cells.

*Alcohol's massive assault on the structure and functioning of the alcoholic's cells cannot be reversed just by removing alcohol from the body–**abstinence alone does not make malnourished cells healthy again.** The cells need vitamins, minerals, amino acids, proteins, fats, and carbohydrates, and they need them in therapeutic amounts and proportions. Without an adequate supply of these nutrients, the cells cannot get on with the long process of repairing the damage done by excessive drinking.*

*Most recovering alcoholics do not even know that they are suffering from nutritional damage. Even if informed about their condition, they probably do not realize that a **balanced diet and nutritional supplements** will help them make a rapid and complete recovery. James R. Milam, Ph.D.*

In February 2017, the Environmental Protection Agency (EPA) listed over 85,000 chemicals in its inventory of substances that fall under the Toxic Substances Control Act (TSCA). The agency is struggling to handle which of those chemicals are in the marketplace today and how they are being used. Our bodies are challenged with these chemicals exposed to us in our air, water, electronics, and everyday household items such as furniture, flooring, plastics, and food. We are exposed to toxins daily; our bodies are built to process a specific toxic load each day by flushing out chemicals and toxins through our liver, lungs, kidneys, and skin.

We run into problems with over-exposure to these toxins; our bodies simply cannot keep up. The liver is the organ responsible for organizing toxins that enter our body. It is essential to detox the liver for those in recovery from addiction to drugs and alcohol. When the liver is compromised and overloaded, it takes the excess toxins and wraps them up to store in a fat cell. Hence so many people have trouble ridding fat in certain places. Fat cells cannot be burned while they are protecting and holding onto toxins. These toxins will be released when we detox from the majority of these chemicals, and an effective way to achieve this is by eating a clean diet.

The skin is the body's last resort and least efficient detox organ. When we experience blemishes, rashes, or discoloration on the skin, our body is starting to get desperate.

Excess toxins cause many symptoms, including but not limited to poor sleep quality, lack of energy, indigestion, upset stomach, diarrhea, constipation, irregular bowel movements, belly bloat, and belly fat, and PMS. Detoxing these chemicals can reduce or diminish these symptoms for good. Unfortunately, many of us have learned or believe that we are supposed to experience some of these symptoms. We consider them normal to some degree, but that is not true! We can minimize discomfort and heal ourselves. Our bodies can operate at optimal capacity if we just let them. Suffering IS optional.

It is essential to understand what happens when toxins are eliminated and we feed our bodies properly with nutrient-dense foods. A clean diet provides innumerable benefits: decreased cravings, increased energy, better digestion, clarity of mind, clear skin, better sleep, increased sex drive, weight loss, discovering food sensitivities, and becoming less dependent on certain foods making the body sick.

When we cease eating toxin-laden foods and switch to a whole foods diet, our liver can activate toxins stuck in fat cells throughout the body (this also applies to seemingly thin folks). Once toxins are re-activated, they move through the bloodstream and are then released. When this process happens, the body can burn up and discard the fat cell storing the toxins. If we do not address our diet, the continuation of all these problematic symptoms will continue. What we resist, persists!

Have you ever noticed you crave what you just ate? When you start eating junk like processed foods, complex carbs, and sugar, you crave more of those foods. You can re-wire your brain to start thinking of food as fuel. Re-wiring the brain changes the thought process. When we eat nutrient-dense, whole foods, there are no fad diets or calorie counting needed. Your body will start craving vegetables, healthy fats, and proteins instead of sugary coffee drinks, salty chips, and pastries.

I have outlined some simple and practical tips to give you guidance and suggestions in the following pages. The lined space below each suggestion is intended for you to take notes or jot down ideas. Write down the thoughts that enter your mind as you move through the pages of this workbook to implement your action plan.

1. DRINK MORE WATER

Did you know that the human brain is 85% water?

The human body is composed of 25% solid matter and 75% water.

When we deprive body cells of water, they start to react differently. Stunningly, many of our backaches, headaches and digestive problems may result from dehydration alone.

Coffee, tea, soda, alcohol, and energy drinks are **not water**. These drinks contain water but also contain dehydrating agents. Do not treat dehydration with these drinks; have a glass of water before indulging in other liquids.

How much water do we need? Some say drink when thirsty, some say eight cups per day, and others recommend up to 15 cups per day. Your water needs are based on age, activity, climate, diet, and health concerns.

An excellent way to gauge water intake is to drink half your body weight in fluid ounces. For example, a person weighing 160 pounds would drink approximately 80 fluid ounces of water per day. As a guide, keep an eye on your urine. It should be plentiful, pale in color, and odorless. If you are not used to drinking water regularly, start by replacing one of your other drinks (sodas or coffees) with a fresh glass of water.

Symptoms of not enough water can be expressed by fatigue, hunger, headaches, sugar cravings, or confusion. Symptoms of too much water often disrupt sleep and mineral imbalances.

Water is the foundation of life and generates life on the planet.
- We should not treat thirst with medication.
- Experiment with water as a natural treatment for ailments.
- Understand how hydration will empower you to be healthy.
- Take charge and become your own healer by feeding your body the water it needs.

Water hydrates the body and helps the kidneys flush toxins naturally. Extra water encourages urine production, flushing out toxic waste. Water also acts as an appetite suppressant; you will be less likely to overeat or reach for the cookies when drinking a glass of water first. Drinking enough water lowers your chance for a strong urge of cravings.

Try drinking approximately eight ounces of water 20 minutes before each meal. Water fills you up, leaving less chance of overeating.

Infuse water by adding lemon, lime, orange slices, berries, cucumber; combine with spices such as parsley, cilantro, or basil for an exciting blend. Search the internet for infused or spa water recipes to get inspired. Then, make it a treat that you look forward to enjoying.

Start your day with warm (not hot) lemon water. Drink a cup as soon as you get up in the morning before anything else. Adopting this habit brings fantastic health benefits.

Although lemon juice is acidic, its low-sugar and high alkaline mineral content have an alkalizing effect. Our bodies have different acidity levels and alkalinity; learning to strike the right balance between the two is one of the keys to good health. Our stomachs are naturally a little more acidic with their digestive juices. A diet high in acidic foods such as white bread, soda, processed fast foods, and to a lesser extent, animal meat and eggs. Your body starts siphoning off minerals such as calcium to neutralize the acid, decreasing the body's ability to absorb essential nutrients to produce energy, repair cells, and detoxify itself.

An acidic system can increase your risk of many degenerative diseases, from arthritis to heart disease to cancer. Use a straw when drinking acidic liquids to help prevent decay of enamel on teeth.

This ritual stimulates your liver, the main detoxing organ in the body that is responsible for having hundreds of vital functions. A healthy liver leads to brighter and clearer skin, clear eyes, a balanced weight, and a better attitude. The liver is most active in the morning, and the lemon helps speed up the elimination of toxins. Do not be surprised if you feel the need to use the bathroom rather quickly; this indicates the process is working.

Lemon water increases your fat-burning capabilities by improving your digestion. If your digestion is not working up to par, it is nearly impossible to shed pounds and keep your weight in check. Warm lemon water stimulates saliva sending a signal to the body to get digestion rolling and help reduce unhealthy cravings.

Lemons possess essential health-building nutrients. One is vitamin C. This excellent vitamin fights cell damage, chronic inflammation strengthens immune defenses, and accelerates wound healing.

If you cannot tolerate lemons try adding apple cider vinegar to warm water. This powerhouse vinegar has been used for centuries as a natural remedy to cure allergies (including allergies to pets, foods, and the environment), sinus infections, acne, high cholesterol, flu, chronic fatigue, candida, acid reflux, sore throats, arthritis, and gout.

We are all unique, and different approaches work for each of us to achieve our goals. So first, determine a good strategy that works for you. Water apps, measurable fun tumblers, fancy water bottles, and containers make it easy to accomplish your water goals. A simple strategy might be to use rubber bands on a 16-ounce tumbler to ensure your daily water intake. If 60 ounces is your goal, you start with four rubber bands, taking one-off each time you fill your container until you have reached your daily goal.

Using the formula of half your body weight in fluid ounces, calculate how much water you would need to drink daily. (Example: 160 pounds divided by 2 = 80 fluid ounces)

_____

What are three ways you can put into action to increase your water consumption?

1._____

_____

_____

2._____

_____

_____

3._____

_____

_____

How do you feel about increasing your water intake?

_____

_____

What roadblocks might you encounter, and how will you keep yourself accountable to overcome these roadblocks?

_____

_____

_____

_____

For further exploration, Fereydoom Batmanghelidj, a best-selling author, has written many books on the curative effects of water.

2. EAT MORE WHOLE VEGGIES AND FRUITS

Focus on eating real food that nourishes the body and increases the body's natural process of functioning. Eat plenty of whole grains, vegetables, fruits, and proteins. Reduce, or stay away from caffeine. Be mindful of inflammatory foods like sugar, dairy, and all things processed. Place intention on eating healthily 90% of the time by following the 90/10 rule!

Shift your perspective to embrace all the delicious foods you can eat instead of what you cannot.

All vegetables and fruits are fair game! Get creative and eat a wide variety; choose dark leafy greens at least once a day. Eating many helpings of dark leafy green vegetables high in magnesium will help keep your energy constant throughout the day. When magnesium levels are even a little low, energy can drop; this is commonly when many people reach for the instant pick-me-up of unhealthy choices such as carbohydrates, sugar, or caffeine.

Think spinach, broccoli, kale. Try incorporating green juices, preferably without added sugars. Fresh juices are a great way to keep the energy up, especially during the mid-afternoon slump or when you feel an illness coming on.

Focus on adding more vegetables to each meal and snacks. Unfortunately, most Americans lack an adequate amount of vegetables in their diet.

Did you know?

Asparagus helps make serotonin and dopamine, helping to regulate mood.

Avocados help lower blood pressure and prevent hypertension.

Dark Leafy Greens like spinach, Swiss chard, collards, and kale are full of magnesium, controlling the release of cortisol.

See Nature's Pharmacy for a complete list of the benefits of vegetables and fruits.

Sprinkle a wide variety of fresh herbs adding a burst of flavor to your food, allowing you to cut back on the salt without sacrificing taste. Herbs and spices have many detoxifying properties and contain a significant number of essential vitamins and minerals. Herbs and spices also provide alkaline minerals that counter the effects of excess acid in the body caused by eating too many acidic foods. Refer to the benefits of herbs and spices in the Nature's Pharmacy to learn the effects they can have on the body.

When you pre-cut vegetables like celery, carrots, radishes, bell peppers, and cucumbers, you will always have something you can quickly grab out of the fridge. Try pairing your vegetables with hummus, black bean dip, or guacamole; adding these healthy fats and proteins will make a great snack, or even a meal, anytime.

In 2017, the USDA reported that white potatoes are the most consumed vegetable due to the high demand for French fries. When menu planning, swap out some white potatoes for starchy more nutrient-dense vegetables like sweet potatoes, yams, and squash.

What three ways can you quickly add more whole vegetables and fruits into your diet?

1._____

_____

_____

2._____

_____

_____

3._____

_____

_____

Do you feel you are an emotional or addictive eater? _____

If Yes, what foods trigger you to over eat? _____

Do you find it tough to give up the very foods that may be causing you the most pain? _____

If you feel dietary changes are complicated or seemingly impossible to conquer, you are not alone. Talk to someone you trust about your challenges or seek a professional trained in nutrition: a health and nutrition coach, an eating disorder specialist, functional medicine, or naturopathic doctor.

What three people come to mind that are trustworthy to discuss your health challenges?

1._____

_____

_____

2._____

_____

_____

3._____

_____

_____

3. EAT AT HOME

Make healthier choices by packing food to take with you. It can take a bit of an effort at first but will soon become a habit. Not only will it lighten your pocketbook, but it will also save you lots of valuable time. Make an effort to eat at home for as many of your meals as possible.

- Take a trip to the grocery store to familiarize yourself with different ingredients.
- Set aside time to clean out unhealthy items in your pantry, refrigerator, and freezer.

Once you start to eat healthy and nutritious foods, you will not want to stop!

The following is a helpful guide to stock your pantry, fridge, and freezer. Keep foods that you love and that love your body back.

CANNED GOODS

- Jars of tomatoes, tomato sauce, and tomato paste
- Variety of canned beans
- Dried lentils and other legumes
- Canned chilies and chipotle in adobo
- Artichokes in water
- Olives
- Sun-dried tomatoes
- Canned chunk light or albacore tuna
- Canned wild salmon
- Broth

FLAVORS AND SEASONINGS

- Apple cider vinegar
- Ume plum vinegar
- Rice vinegar
- Fish sauce
- Hot sauce
- Mustard – Dijon, stone-ground, honey, spicy
- Organic ketchup
- Cold-pressed extra virgin olive oil (for salads and dressings)
- Refined grapeseed, avocado, coconut, or sesame oil (for high heat cooking)
- Toasted sesame oil – flavoring stir-fries
- Onions
- Garlic
- Raw honey
- Sea salt
- Pepper
- Dried herbs and spices: paprika, chili powder, bay leaves, ginger, turmeric, thyme, oregano, cumin, coriander, curry, crushed red pepper, sesame seeds, etc.

PANTRY

- Brown rice
- Basmati rice
- Quinoa
- Quinoa or brown rice pasta
- Cornmeal
- Oatmeal
- Organic tortilla chips
- High quality, gluten-free grain or seed crackers

REFRIGERATOR

- Lemons and limes
- Lettuce
- Carrots
- Leafy greens
- Butternut squash or sweet potatoes
- Avocado
- Assorted mustards
- Organic ketchup
- Organic mayonnaise
- Miso paste
- Free-range, organic eggs
- Raw walnuts, hazelnuts, almonds
- Sprouted corn tortillas, whole grain bread
- Salsa
- Seeds: sunflower, pumpkin, flax

FREEZER

- Assorted organic berries
- Broccoli
- Peas
- Organic spinach
- Free-range meats
- Wild-caught cold-water sustainable fish

When you have a pantry, refrigerator, and freezer full of yummy, healthy foods ready to use and eat, you will be less tempted to stray back to old habits.

If you choose to eat out, order dishes that have lots of vegetables and some lean protein. Ask the server for vegetables steamed instead of sautéed in oil and butter. Most restaurants heavily use unhealthy fats, sugar, and salt to add more flavoring to foods. Minimize or steer clear of dishes that contain heavy sauces and anything fried.

Are you willing to take steps to set yourself up for success?

_____

Which day of the week might you begin to reserve time to do your meal planning and prepping?

_____

_____

What challenges do you anticipate when thinking about preparing more homemade meals at home?

_____

_____

_____

Do time constraints stand in your way and make this seem impossible? If so, put your focus on taking small steps for a successful approach. Although there is more than one way to achieve this, simply purchasing healthy items is a conscientious first step.

4. SKIP OR REDUCE THE SUGAR

Sugar causes abrupt changes in blood sugar levels and aggravates hypoglycemic symptoms. Therefore, avoid or strictly limit refined carbohydrates such as pastries, candies, artificial sugar, and baked goods.

Choose natural sweeteners such as honey, dates, pure maple syrup, agave, and stevia, and use sparingly.

Sugar is a massive issue for people in addiction recovery; we will dive deeper into this topic in the next chapter.

5. DRINK HERBAL TEAS TO REDUCE
OR ELIMINATE CAFFEINE

Most of us do not realize how dependent we are on caffeine; it can indeed be an addiction. However, coffee is not the only option when you need a pick-me-up. Herbal teas provide an all-natural temporary boost of energy without the risk of stimulants or processed ingredients and are delicious warm, or iced.

As with most products, all teas are not created equal. Opting to save a few dollars on cheaper tea can cost you a lot more when it comes to your health.

These common tea brands have been shown to contain high levels of toxic substances such as fluoride and pesticides, artificial ingredients, added flavors, and GMOs (modified corn starch and soy lecithin). The levels found in these products are so high that they are considered unsafe for consumption.

Toxic teas to avoid: Lipton (pure green tea), Allegro, Celestial Seasoning, Tazo, Teavana, Yellow label black tea, Tetley (green tea), Twining's, Republic of Tea, Tea Forte, Mighty Leaf, Trader Joe's Tetley, No Name (black tea), Uncle Lee's Legends of China (green tea and jasmine green tea), King Cole – (Orange Pekoe), Yogi and Allegro (these contain natural flavors that might not be so natural).

The Canadian Broadcasting Corporation (CBC) investigated several popular international tea companies, including Tetley, Lipton, Twining's, No Name, Uncle Lee's Legends of China, King Cole, and Signal.

Alarmingly, the CBC found that these brands contained a level of toxins that exceeded the legal limit.

To keep yourself safe from harmful toxins or pesticides that may be lurking in your cup, and to instead enjoy the incredible health benefits, here are some ways to avoid these chemicals:
- Try switching to white tea. It has the least amount of fluoride due to the use of young leaves.
- Be sure to buy loose leaf tea or brew your tea from scratch.
- Buy organic! Choose a non-GMO-certified brand of tea.
- Check the ingredient list to ensure no added flavors or GMO ingredients have been added to the tea leaves.
- Many restaurants use tea brands that are known to be full of pesticides, so be careful about ordering tea while out to eat.
- Know the correct brewing times for certain types of tea. Black or Pu-reh teas should steep for 3-5 minutes; white or green teas should steep for 2-3 minutes; Oolong teas should steep for 4-7 minutes; and herbal teas should be left to steep for five minutes at a minimum, longer for a stronger tea.

Bagged tea that is found to be safe: Red Rose, Numi Tea, Rishi Tea, EDEN Organic, Organic Stash, Choice Organic, Two Leaves, Organic Tazo, and Organic Traditional Medicinal.

Detox teas such as milk thistle, lemongrass, nettle, ginger, dandelion root, and green tea are great options. In addition, many brands have selections with blends of these herbs, spices, and leaves marketed as detox-ready for purchase and use.

Nettle tea is the bowel mover. A cup of nettle tea in the morning is ideal for getting things going. Nettle leaves increase and release mucus in the colon, allowing for the necessary flushing of excess waste. They also increase thyroid function and your metabolism.

6. ELIMINATE OBVIOUS TOXINS

To fully detox your body, particularly your liver, it is vital to cease consumption of alcohol, tobacco, all illicit drugs, and even certain over-the-counter medications such as Tylenol, ibuprofen, and Excedrin. This is the **only** way you can assist in eliminating waste that could impair cellular function.

NOTE: Always consult with your physician before discontinuing any prescription medication.

For everyday aches and pains, you can ditch over-the-counter ibuprofen for some raw turmeric root or turmeric supplements to help reduce inflammation. Turmeric is a significant source of a polyphenol called curcumin. Polyphenols are antioxidants that help protect the body against free radicals, pathogens, and the effects of UV radiation. Pairing turmeric with black pepper, which contains a substance called piperine, can help your body absorb the curcumin 2,000% better by keeping the curcumin in the body longer. Turmeric supplements are available at most grocery, drug, and health food stores and can be purchased in the root form at many grocery produce sections.

Bromelain, a mixture of enzymes derived from the pineapple fruit or stem, is also helpful for reducing chronic inflammation. Papain is a protein-digesting enzyme obtained from unripe papaya fruit and is used as a supplement to aid in digestion. Both bromelain and papain help heal wounds and reduce inflammation. You can get the natural benefits of these fantastic foods by simply eating raw papaya and pineapple or by taking papaya or bromelain supplements. Whole foods such as kiwifruit, ginger, asparagus, sauerkraut, kimchi, yogurt, and kefir are all additional choices that can reduce inflammation in the body.

_____

_____

_____

7. FIND SUPPORT

Having a support system will increase your success rate. You are much less likely to throw in the towel when you have someone on your side to steer you away from the cookies.

Most of us have tried sheer willpower; you probably already know that this does not work. Often, we end up in worse shape than when we started. If you are active in a recovery program and attend support groups like AA meetings, bring up your struggles in a meeting with your sponsor or a trusted friend. There is a high probability that others have had the same struggles as you and are willing to help. By reaching out to others, you allow someone else to be of service and share their experience, strength, and hope.

Today, there are support groups for almost every kind of suffering known to man. (AA) Alcoholic Anonymous, (NA) narcotics anonymous, (ADAA) Anxiety and Depression Association of America, (MADD) Mothers Against Drunk Drivers, (SLAA) Sex and Love Addicts Anonymous, (SAA) Sex Addicts Anonymous, (EDA) Eating Disorders Anonymous, etc., the list goes on and on.

Be honest with yourself; write out areas in your life where you struggle; relationships, career, substances, food, etc.

_____

_____

_____

Reach out and share your struggles with a trusted person; everyone needs support to get through life's trials and tribulations. You are not alone!

8. SET HEALTHY BOUNDARIES

Overcommitment leads to fatigue, leading to poor food choices.

Try to streamline your list of must-do activities, including professional, family, and social obligations.

Set priorities in terms of the most important tasks first. Your recovery program should top the list before family, friends, and work. Then, when you are spiritually and emotionally fit, you will show up for others feeling your best.

Permit yourself to prioritize self-care. Without your good health, you will have nothing worthwhile.

Assess your energy. Before doing anything with another person, whether you are spending time one-on-one or chatting on the phone, check in with yourself. How is your current mood? Are you feeling vibrant and positive? Or are you feeling exhausted and depleted? Knowing how you are already feeling brings some perspective to the situation. If you are already tired, being around someone draining your energy will not likely be a recipe for clear communication. Make sure you know where you are emotionally before engaging with someone else.

Know your role. You can support people you love; however, you cannot fix their problems no matter how much you want. They are the only ones who can choose to continue leading the life they are currently in or not. Know who you are in the relationship. You are not responsible for others, be it their actions, words, mood, or perspective. They are responsible for themselves.

How would it feel to set loving boundaries to prevent building new resentments?
(Scary, impossible?)

_____

_____

To whom do you perceive the most difficult to set boundaries, and why? (Spouse, parents, boss)

_____

_____

What obstacles do you foresee?

_____

_____

_____

By accessing your energy first and knowing your role in the relationship, how can you set boundaries with love and at the same time uphold respect for yourself and others?

_____

_____

_____

Be confident in setting new boundries. It can be challenging to feel like you are making these decisions for yourself. Fear will tell you that you are insensitive or do not love that person enough. But this is not true. On the contrary, you love them so much that you are taking care of your own needs to have a great relationship with them, helping to prevent future resentments in all your relationships.

9. EXERCISE DAILY

Sweat releases impurities from the body during exercise, making it a natural choice for regular detoxification.

Engaging in physical activity sends oxygen and nutrients to your body's cells. As a result, it helps your heart and lungs work more efficiently and boost energy levels.

Focus on taking walks outdoors when weather permits, stretching exercises, and low-impact activities like yoga or Pilates. Look to see if your local gyms offer discounts for new students. Connect with people that have similar interests, which will, in turn, hold you accountable for showing up.

If you opt for intensive workouts, be sure to compensate by drinking extra water and snacking on high-protein foods like chia seeds, walnuts, almonds, organic chicken, or turkey slices.

If you currently do not participate in any type of exercise, think about why that is. What excuses do you tell yourself for not making exercise part of your schedule?

_____

_____

_____

What physical activities do you enjoy or activities that you enjoyed in the past?

_____

_____

_____

What type of exercise or activities have you always wanted to try but have put off for one reason or another?

_____

_____

_____

Who can you recruit to be your workout buddy?

_____

_____

_____

Make it a priority to reach out to someone and set up an activity date. Getting something on your calendar is the best way to make this happen. Now, give them a call!

10. TAKE A LOOK AT GLUTEN, DAIRY, AND RED MEAT

GLUTEN products such as bread, pasta, rye, and bagels, have become a staple in most American households. But, unfortunately, these products do not offer much or any nutritional value.

From a scientific perspective, the food-mood relationship is maintained by neurotransmitters – chemical messengers that relay thoughts and actions throughout the brain and gut. Some neurotransmitters, such as serotonin, can make us feel relaxed. Others, such as dopamine, have a stimulating effect. The food we eat breaks down in the digestive tract enters the bloodstream, and produces these neurotransmitters, thus impacting our mood. For example, eating carbohydrates such as those mentioned above releases serotonin in the brain, making people feel more relaxed. On the other hand, eating too many carbs or overly processed carbs, like sugar and flour, releases even more serotonin, causing drowsiness. You have probably experienced that sleepy feeling after overeating pasta or heavy carbohydrates.

It is essential to eat appropriate protein portions, as protein produces dopamine and norepinephrine in the brain, making people feel more alert with an abundance of energy. But, at the same time, being mindful not to over-consume protein can lead to tension and irritability.

The goal is to find balance for yourself, not what society tells you.

Look for ancient grains like amaranth, wheat berry, and quinoa, to name a few – these grains have higher nutritional value. The idea here is to expand your choices away from the standard overabundance of whole wheat and white rice, which are commonly frequent selections.

If you choose a gluten-free diet and purchase prepackaged (processed) products, be aware of possible higher sugar and salt content. These foods are not your ideal way to achieve a gluten-free lifestyle.

Recommended resources are included in the back of this book with in-depth information from nutrition specialists in these fields.

Take a closer look at your food choices. How much gluten does your diet include?

_____

_____

_____

DAIRY is problematic for most people to digest; many studies conclude numbers to be as high as 75-80% of the population. Most people do not realize that some of their health issues may be related to their dairy consumption. Therefore, it is beneficial to experiment for yourself. Why not see how it feels to be dairy-free? Try eliminating dairy for seven days and then slowly add it back in; pay attention to how you feel after having a glass of milk or a piece of cheese.

Casein is a protein found in milk and other dairy products. A casein allergy occurs when your body mistakenly identifies casein as a threat to your body. Your body then triggers a reaction in an attempt to fight it off, this is different than lactose intolerance, which occurs when your body does not make enough of the enzyme lactase. In addition, casein releases casomorphins, plant compounds that trigger dopamine production in your brain. Dairy is mildly addictive and challenging for many to give up.

Dairy today is not what it used to be. It has been found to be bad for the environment due to cows raised in feedlots. Dairy is not well tolerated by most people (except Northern Europeans and the Masai people) because 75% of the world's population is lactose intolerant. The way we raise dairy cattle is terrible for the cows, the environment, and humans. Dairy has been linked to cancer, osteoporosis, autoimmune diseases, allergic disorders, digestive problems, and more. Some studies have shown that reduced risk of type 2 diabetes, heart disease, and stroke are among the benefits of eliminating or reducing dairy consumption.

An alternative is to find dairy that contains A2 casein, produced from heirloom cows, for it does not cause the same digestive or inflammatory problems as modern cow products. You can also experiment with goat or sheep dairy instead of cow dairy as they also contain A2 casein—some producers, such as organic pasture-raised grass-finished A2 cow milk. Always choose organic and 100% grass-fed.

Many food manufacturers heavily use sugars to enhance the flavor in dairy and dairy-free alternatives such as coconut, hemp, almond, or soy. Therefore, pay attention to sugar content with your chosen selections.

Organic and non-GMO are always your best choices, especially when it comes to nuts and soy; these are some of the most heavily pesticidal sprayed crops. For more information, go to www.ewg.org

List some dairy products, and the quantity you consume daily or regularly.

_____

_____

_____

What feelings come up when you think about abstaining from dairy for even a short time?

_____

_____

_____

By using the food journal format contained in chapter 5, you can do experiments for yourself. If you eliminate dairy for as little as five days, reintroduce the individual foods back into your diet and then write out how they make you feel, it can give you a clear picture of whether dairy affects you or not.

Think about your health concerns, whether it be achy joints, arthritis, headaches, etc. Think about how they may be connected to your diet.

_____

_____

_____

RED MEAT and PORK are harder on the digestive system to break down than other sources of protein. Commit to more meals with protein sources obtained from chicken, turkey, wild-caught cold-water fish, beans, or lentils. Choose grass-fed, pasteurized, and organic meats-they have more nutrients in them than conventionally raised animals.

Choose regeneratively raised animal products whenever possible. Regenerative agriculture is a conservation and rehabilitation approach to food and farming systems. It focuses on topsoil regeneration, increasing biodiversity, improving the water cycle, enhancing ecosystem services, supporting bio-sequestration, increasing resilience to climate change, and strengthening the health and vitality of farm soil. For more information, pick up a copy of *Food Fix, How to Save Our Health, Our Economy, Our Communities, and Our Planet – One Bite at a Time*, by Mark Hyman, MD.

Notice your food attachments with gluten, dairy, and red meat. Having awareness is the first step to making necessary changes. Then, look at your choices from a new perspective. Many people have attachments to certain foods, whether sugar, salty chips, or a cup of coffee. Learn to identify your food attachments.

Making dietary modifications can be overwhelming; ask for help to overcome nutritional changes that might better serve your wellbeing.

As you become aware of your choices, make it a habit to pause before reaching for that food that may be bringing discomfort in the long run. Ask yourself if you are looking for a snack because you are truly hungry, or is it because you need a distraction?

What is the one healthy food you can commit to adding to your diet? Choose something that may have worked for you in the past. Build on that success!

_____

_____

_____

Stay accountable by writing down and sharing your goals with another person. Research shows that when we have someone to hold us accountable, there is over a 40% increased success rate in achieving goals and dreams. The likelihood that you will transform your desires into reality goes up even further if you share your written goals with a friend who believes in your ability to succeed.

List three people or sources you may use to hold you accountable to reach your nutritional goals.

1._____

2._____

3._____

If you feel yourself slipping, do not get discouraged and do not give up! Instead, adapt to the 90/10 diet, eating nutritionally dense foods most of the time, allowing yourself to indulge occasionally.

"I'm like a recovering perfectionist.
For me, it's one day at a time."

- BRENE BROWN

CHAPTER 2: CURBING SUGAR CRAVINGS

Most of us have a complex and challenging relationship with sugar. Understanding what sugar does to our bodies and why we have intense sugar cravings is crucial to tackling strong cravings when they arise.

Sugar cravings are simply the body asking for energy. When we consume sugar, it swiftly enters the bloodstream, wreaking havoc on blood sugar levels, soon after causing uncontrollable cravings, nervous tension, and hyperactivity, followed by fatigue, depression, and exhaustion. We start riding this emotional rollercoaster, feeling happy and energetic for a while, and then suddenly finding ourselves feeling irritated and not quite right. Sound familiar?

Our body wants to maintain balanced blood sugar, signaling us to eat something to bring blood sugar levels back up. Typically blood sugar levels drop around midafternoon, or a few hours after lunch, signaling us to eat again!

For people who struggle with addiction, unstable blood sugar levels often lead to conscious cravings, an impulse to drink, or use drugs.

While people may mistakenly use the diagnosis of hypoglycemia to explain unrelated psychological and emotional problems, there is no question that the great majority of alcoholics suffer from chronic low blood sugar. When given the 5-hour glucose tolerance test, 95% of both early and late-stage alcoholics experience a spike in blood sugar level after sugar intake and then a rapid plunge. If their erratic blood sugar level is not controlled, alcoholics suffer chronic depression, irritability, anguish, fatigue, insomnia, headaches, and mental confusion. Worst of all, low blood sugar causes a craving for alcohol and sweets, which can quickly raise blood sugar and relieve the symptoms. Sober alcoholics, therefore, must learn to control their sugar intake to avoid mood fluctuations, anxiety, depression, and recurring impulses to drink.

However, the healing process can take several years, and if the alcoholic neglects his diet after months of sobriety, his body will have a difficult time completing the repair work. Moreover, because some of the damage – in the liver and elsewhere – is often permanent, it will need continued supplementation to offset continued deficiencies. In addition, low blood sugar will remain a chronic condition that will surface continually unless it is controlled through diet. For all these reasons, nutrition should be emphasized from the start of recovery. James R. Milam, Ph.D.

Sugar has become a large part of the daily diet and consequently, so have chronic diseases. One of the most alarming statistics in medicine today is the rate at which people are diagnosed with type 2 diabetes, and sugar has a direct link to this disease. Simply reducing processed sugar and eating a healthy balanced diet can prevent this condition.

The USDA recommends no more than nine teaspoons of sugar per day for men: for women, it is six teaspoons. Thus, most Americans eat about three times that liberally recommended daily value. To put this in perspective, there are 4 grams of sugar per teaspoon, so an item with 36 grams is a man's daily limit. Here is a quick reference of just how much sugar is in some popular drink choices; a 12-ounce Coca-Cola has 39 grams, 12-ounce Fanta orange soda has 44 grams, and a 16-ounce Frappuccino has 55 grams.

Sadly, many food manufacturers use added sugars to add flavor and appeal and to extend shelf life.

Refined sugars digest quickly, causing blood glucose spikes and crashes that lead to cravings and weight gain. Our cells do not require large amounts of glucose simultaneously, so the extra sugar is stored as fat. The body does not absorb refined sugars properly and creates nutrient deficiencies due to the lack of vitamins, minerals, and fiber.

Sugar occurs naturally in all foods containing complex carbohydrates: fruits, vegetables, dairy, and whole grains. These foods also contain fiber or protein, or both. Our bodies digest these sugars more slowly, resulting in a steady supply of glucose, or fuel to our cells, providing long-lasting energy.

Sugar qualifies as an addictive substance for two reasons,
1) Eating even a tiny amount creates a desire for more.
2) Quitting suddenly causes withdrawal symptoms such as headaches, cravings, mood swings, and fatigue.

Research shows that intense sweet flavors are as addictive as cocaine to our bodies. We are left addicted and wanting more.

Your life can be completely different if you decide to make nutritional changes. You can get off the sugar rollercoaster and **reduce cravings naturally**. By reducing sugar intake, you will lower the risk of various health problems such as, hypoglycemia, blood sugar spikes, anxiety and depression, irritability and mood swings, weight gain, and overall bodily pain.

Sugary snacks may provide temporary energy or satisfy that sweet tooth, though often, we end up feeling more tired.

A sweet treat now and then will not hurt; however, the brain is hardwired to be addicted to sugar, just like a drug. It makes you want more until suddenly, no amount is enough.

Focus on making daily choices to live a happier and healthier life. Follow the 90/10 rule, choosing nutritionally dense foods 90% of the time. We all deserve to feel great!

Let us dig into some simple tips to reduce your dependence on unhealthy processed sugar and create a success of kicking the sugar habit for good.

1. LAY OFF THE SUGAR

Crowding out is a concept that occurs when we add healthy foods to our diet; in doing this, we crowd out unhealthy cravings. For example, merely drinking more water and eating more dark leafy greens often results in gaining control over cravings.

A helpful rule to follow would be to eat nutritionally dense foods first, leaving less room for unhealthy treats. We are all unique and need to figure out what works best for each of us. A successful plan for some people might look like eating healthily during the week, Monday through Friday, and being more relaxed with choices on the weekends. For others, saving 10% to indulge at celebrations, group gatherings, barbeques, or dining out, works well.

Laying off sugar may seem impossible, though I assure you, it is not. You can naturally reduce your sugar intake by making a small conscious decision, for example; limit or avoiding coffee drinks like mochas and Frappuccino's, candy, cookies, and most desserts.

Cravings come from foods that we have recently eaten. Often, after one sip or bite, your body will crave more of that food. You probably have noticed increased cravings for sweets after having more desserts and sweets than usual during the holidays increases.

Seek out low sugar or healthier alternatives by making conscious choices and choosing 70% (or higher) dark chocolate versus milk chocolate and fresh fruit versus pastries and cakes. These small changes can make a massive difference to irresistible cravings for more intense sweet foods. Small quantities are okay; moderation is key. Unfortunately, as a society, we tend to indulge way too much, and it often comes in the form of sneaky sugar.

Nearly 70% of our diet's added sugar comes from processed foods, such as salad dressings, bread, pasta sauces, and peanut butter, all significant contributors. To avoid these sneaky sugars, seek out products with fewer ingredients listed on the label. Likewise, be sure you can identify the ingredients listed as real food.

Chew your food thoroughly to taste what you are eating. Chewing creates enzymes necessary for digestion.

When would you use your ten% of indulgence, and for what occasions?

_____

_____

What obstacles do you foresee encountering when you think about reducing sugar?

_____

_____

Do you feel you are addicted to sugar? _____

If you feel you struggle with sugar addiction, what foods might be the toughest to reduce or eliminate?

_____

_____

2. DO NOT SKIP MEALS

It is essential to learn to listen to your body. Enjoy breakfast, lunch, and dinner; this allows your metabolism to work efficiently. Eating every 4-5 hours, even a tiny amount of nutrient-dense foods will keep blood sugar leveled.

Most Americans tend to overeat. Instead, eat to be satisfied, portion control your meals, rewire the brain to eat when your body needs energy. The salivary glands produce enzymes necessary to break down carbohydrates and fat, making it easier to allow the digestive system to work correctly.

Eating too fast can cause poor nutrient absorption, leading to heartburn, constipation, and acid reflux. When you chew your food slowly, you secrete more salvia, soften the food, and change its texture. The vitamins and minerals are absorbed by salvia; these vitamins and minerals will boost your body's energy. Your brain sends signals that make you feel full. The urge to eat reduces excessive weight gain and will aid in weight loss.

When you chew your food correctly, it also benefits your mouth, improving oral hygiene. Salvia helps fight mouth odor and plaque. Hydrogen carbonate in salvia neutralizes plaque formation, kills harmful bacteria, and washes away food particles around the teeth.

Eat while you are present, not distracted with television or electronics of any kind; your brain will experience the joy of eating Practice giving thanks before diving into your meal.

What are your typical daily food choices? What time do you often eat meals throughout your day?

Breakfast _____

_____

_____

Lunch _____

_____

_____

Dinner _____

_____

_____

A food journal format is included in chapter 5. Here you can record any differences you experience with your digestion. Knowledge is power!

3. BALANCE YOUR MEALS

Our body naturally wants to be balanced. The choices of food we eat are a major contributing factor to the overall balance of the body. When looking at a meal or a snack, think **Fat + Fiber + Protein.**

Vegetables and whole grains have mild effects on the body. However, meat, dairy, sugar, and salt have extreme effects, throwing off the body's balance. Seek out less radical and healthier alternatives to satisfy hunger and stop the damaging cycle.

Cravings are the body's solution to underlying imbalances. Our body craves whatever the body needs to regain balance. For example, eating a lot of meat may cause more sugar cravings.

Sneak in more protein to meals and snacks; this keeps blood sugar levels steady and reduces sugar cravings. Conversely, protein imbalances can cause intense sugar cravings.

How much and what types of protein to consume are highly debated. Some say that high-quality animal protein is needed for optimal health, while others advocate for a plant-based diet—experiment with what works for your body. You will then be able to guide yourself to your appropriate protein source successfully.

Think beyond the cow and chicken. Be creative with other sources: quinoa, beans, nuts, eggs, dark green vegetables, and fish.

Signs of low protein intake can be muscle and joint pain, slow recovery from injuries, fluid retention, brain fog, getting sick often, even hair, nail, and skin troubles are associated. Too much protein can also have adverse effects, causing weight gain, high cholesterol, organ damage, and digestive problems.

Do you pay any attention to how much fat, fiber, and protein you consume? _____

Now that you have a greater awareness of the connection between sugar cravings and a balanced diet, will you be more likely to make different choices?

_____

_____

_____

What sources of proteins do you frequently choose?

_____

_____

_____

Which sources of proteins are you willing to experiment with?

_____

_____

_____

4. EAT YOUR VEGGIES

We have intense cravings when our body is starved for vitamins and minerals. Cravings for more and more food mean the cells are starved for vitamins and minerals and suffer from malnutrition. Malnutrition is commonly found in the earliest stages of alcoholics and addicts, along with many other diseases.

When we put focus on vegetables at each meal, we can **crowd out** unhealthy sugary cravings. Eating lots of veggies leaves less room for the processed, nutrient-deficient foods. When we fill our bodies with vegetables first, cravings for unhealthy foods will lessen substantially. Our bodies really can only hold so much food; it is difficult to eat five fruits and vegetables a day and then binge on ice cream.

Amazing things happen when we consistently make better choices; the body will naturally begin to crave what you eat, even the healthier options. Adopt the 90/10 rule!

It is exciting when you feel the effects and experience switching from sugar to healthy green foods.

What are three ways you can easily incorporate more vegetables into your meals?

1. _____

2. _____

3. _____

5. SQUASH CRAVINGS WITH SWEET VEGETABLES

Long before food processing, the only source of sweet foods was from plants such as squashes, sweet potatoes, yams, carrots, onions, beets, fruits, and many spices, think cinnamon, cardamom, nutmeg.

Sweet vegetables are also an excellent source of nutrients, energy, and fiber, all needed to maintain good health. Incorporating many of these lovely foods is one of the best ways to alleviate increased sugar cravings. Provide your body with the sweetness it needs by regularly eating naturally sweet foods.

Sweet vegetables soothe the internal organs and energize the mind. Many of these sweet foods are root vegetables and also energetically grounding. They help balance the spaced-out feeling often felt after eating sweet foods that are highly processed. To crowd out intense sugar cravings, add in many sweet vegetables regularly.

Be creative – steam, roast, grill, boil, stir-fry. These sweet vegetables create delicious soups, can be eaten raw, and can be grated into salads. When you roast large batches, you can keep them ready for a quick meal or side dish; this can be a huge time saver for busy lifestyles. Pair them with your favorite grain and some healthy fats like half of an avocado for a fast, nutritious meal at home or on the go.

Include semi-sweet vegetables such as turnips, parsnips, rutabagas, and perhaps subtly sweet vegetables such as red radishes, daikon, green cabbage, and burdock. It can be fun to search online to be inspired by new ideas, especially if some foods are new to you.

Your fruits and vegetables will taste sweeter when you add a dash of Himalayan or sea salt and will open your taste buds.

When we nourish ourselves with sweet vegetables and fruits, the need for sugar from candy, pastries, or sodas lessens substantially.

Commit to trying a new vegetable each time you meal plan or when you do your grocery shopping. There are recipes at the back of this book to be inspired.

Which sweet vegetables have you never eaten that sound intriguing? There is a full list to refer to in the vegetable section in the *Nature's Pharmacy* chapter at the back of this book.

_____

_____

_____

6. AVOID THE FAKE STUFF –
ARTIFICIAL SWEETENERS

Artificial ingredients also affect blood sugar levels that are linked to severe health problems.

If you are trying to lose weight, drinking diet sodas is not the solution. The artificial sweeteners they contain have proved to stimulate appetite, increase carbohydrate cravings, and promote fat storage and weight gain. In addition, researchers from the University of Texas at Houston discovered that drinking diet sodas would expand your waist, a risk factor for type 2 diabetes.

A study reported in the American Journal of Clinical Nutrition suggests that a daily diet soda habit (at least one per day) could hurt your circulatory system and increase the possibility of vascular events such as stroke and heart attack.

Aspartame is considered one of the most dangerous substances allowed in our food supply. Researchers have found that aspartame raised blood sugar. In addition to diabetes, aspartame is linked to autoimmune disorders, depression (which can cause you to eat more), congenital disabilities, and several forms of cancer.

Another prominent suspect is **Erythritol**, a sugar alcohol found in many products. The body does not easily digest sugar alcohols, and as a result, it can cause diarrhea, headache, and other intestinal disorders.

Acesulfame potassium, or **Ace-K**, is found in many popular diet drinks. According to the Center for Science in the Public Interest (CSPI), this product is anything but safe. Studies suggested that the additive might cause cancer, but the FDA never addressed these studies before it approved the sweetener for use in soft drinks. Large doses of acetoacetamide have been shown to affect the thyroid. As you might know, the thyroid gland regulates the endocrine system, responsible for a healthy metabolism.

Cannot go cold turkey? Try cutting back by a fourth the first week, half the second week, and so on, until you can quit your soda habit for good.

Make substitutions.
- Sparkling water
- Sparkling water + lime juice + organic cranberry juice
- Water + cucumbers + strawberries
- Sparkling water + lemon juice + fresh-pressed organic orange juice
- Probiotic drinks
- Raw coconut water
- Cold-brewed organic tea

Use safe, natural sweeteners for coffee and teas (choose organic when possible)
- Raw local honey
- Stevia
- Pure maple syrup
- Blackstrap molasses
- Agave syrup

Try to avoid or significantly reduce the use of white or brown sugars—the palate changes when elimination occurs, resulting in fewer sweet cravings with reduced consumption.

Be aware that sugar-free and fat-free on product labels usually mean artificial sweeteners are in them.

The body does not know how to assimilate these artificial chemicals. Research shows that these substitutes can cause weight gain by stimulating the appetite and increasing the body's fat storage capabilities, even though they are touted as diet products.

Knowledge and awareness are the first steps to taking action to eliminate harmful chemicals!

Do you use artificial sweeteners regularly? List the ones you use here, then look up these sweeteners in the *Ingredients to Avoid* chapter and be familiar with what these additives contain in them.

_____

_____

_____

_____

7. BE A LABEL READER

Many so-called healthy foods contain sugar. A classic example would be energy or protein bars; many people believe that these are healthy and even good choices, not all protein bars are created equal. You might be surprised to learn that a lemon poppy seed *Cliff Bar* has 21 grams of sugar or five teaspoons. Compare that to a chocolate-glazed cake donut from Dunkin Donuts, which has 13 grams of sugar or three teaspoons. Product marketing positions certain foods in our mind to be a naturally healthy choice; this seriously misleads consumers.

Overconsumption of these refined sweets and added sugars found in everyday processed foods has led to increased chronic diseases.

Duke University Medical Center suggests avoiding food items where sugar (or any form of starch) is listed in the first five ingredients or has more than 4 grams of sugar.

Sugar is often disguised in fancy language using many aliases, corn syrup, lactose, dextrose, maltose, glucose, and fructose. Anything ending with an -ose is typically a sweetener.

Sugar aliases include Barbados sugar, barley malt, brown rice syrup, caramel, dextran, diastase, ethyl malt, golden sugar, hydrolyzed starch, malt, maltodextrin, Maltotroise, mannitol, muscovado, sorbitol, sorghum syrup, starch, and treacle. For the complete list, refer to https://mindfulketo.com/sugar-aliases/.

Make informed choices; know what is actually in the items you chose to put into your body.

Take a look in your pantry. Which packaged products do you regularly purchase?

_____

_____

_____

Look at some of the ingredients in these products and the list below, listing the grams of sugar each contains per serving.

_____

_____

_____

_____

Which items are you shocked to discover the high sugar content?

_____

_____

_____

What items might you avoid or limit to control sugar intake?

_____

_____

_____

8. LISTEN TO YOUR CRAVINGS

Our body sends messages through discomfort or food cravings. These messages need to be decoded. For example, cravings such as sugar may mean you need a meeting, are dissatisfied with a relationship, are stressed, or are uninspired. Trust your body and listen to your cravings messages; these cues can support your recovery from addiction.

Are you dehydrated or need some protein? When we learn to home in and listen to our body's intuition, it tells us what we need!

Spending too much time in front of a computer screen, not drinking enough water, or drinking too much coffee, all of these messages are too important for us to ignore.

Keep a craving journal to identify your habits that commonly lead to cravings and rate the craving intensity from 1 to 10. Note your thoughts and the type of craving that comes up. Remember, the first step to changing old habits is the awareness that you have specific patterns. Next, think about why you may be having that particular craving. Cravings are not the underlying problem. Learn to decode what your body is telling you! Your sponsor, therapist, and support friends can help you sift through these issues. Avoid keeping secrets and talk about your challenges, support groups are safe places for this.

Many of us have been taught to believe that our inability to stick with a diet is a weakness, or a flaw in our body, or of our will. This is NOT TRUE; just like a drug or alcohol, sugar is also addictive.

Cravings are not a weakness; they are important messages meant to help us maintain balance. Learn to trust your body's cues and think of cravings as your friend instead of the enemy.

Below, list common foods you crave. Think about the time of day or what is happening in your life when you have cravings. (example: sugary treats in the afternoon or an afternoon slump. solution: apple + nut butter for a snack, versus a candy bar or chips)

_____

_____

_____

Do you see a link between your cravings and your choices?

_____

Give yourself a break and distract yourself. Be patient; wait 20 minutes to evaluate the true craving; it may not be food after all!

When an intense craving comes your way, distract your brain by taking a walk, playing a game, or calling a friend. If you are at work, see if you can take a real break by going outside to disengage. You may find that you are stressed or that you have just been sitting for far too long.

What are new ways you are willing to try to distract yourself from your sugar cravings?

_____

_____

_____

After a 20 minute active break, you may find that you are indeed hungry; make mindful choices of nutrient-dense snacks instead of sugar-loaded carbs. A glass of water, apple slices with nut butter, or a trail mix, are easy snacks to pack for whatever kind of day you may have planned.

9. FEEL THE DIFFERENCE IN WHAT YOU EAT

What we eat affects how we think, feel, and act. Food goes into our stomach as it digests and is absorbed into our blood. Our blood is what creates our cells, tissues, organs, and even our thoughts. We think differently when we eat meat versus broccoli or when we drink a cup of coffee versus alcohol. Stop and think for a moment about how you feel throughout the day. Do you sometimes feel like you have brain fog? Are you tired after lunch? Are you angry and irritable between meals? Or maybe you are energized by a great meal? Feel the difference in the moods that prompt you to eat certain kinds of foods. What is your mood craving?

_____

_____

The Standard American Diet or SAD (such a fitting acronym) is high in processed carbohydrates and generally poor-quality animal meat, lacking in vegetables, healthy fats, and water. SAD leaves many people in a bad mood. It is difficult to feel inspired, light-spirited, or happy when you live on chemically induced, artificial junk food. Many nutritionists refer to this relationship as the law of malnutrition, where someone could be overweight but also malnourished.

People want to be lifted out of a bad mood and gain energy. The irony is that we tend to reach for the very foods that are a big part of the problem. Your blood sugar goes up, and you get that "woo-hoo" good feeling, but then it comes crashing down; you are left in a vicious cycle. Create an action plan to get yourself off this sugar rollercoaster for good.

Make the connection of how different foods affect you. Give yourself the freedom to choose foods that nourish you and to live the life you deserve. By doing this, you will reduce or eliminate anxiety, cravings, bodily aches, and pains.

Most people are dehydrated, do not eat enough vegetables, are sleep deprived, and lack exercise or movement.

Can you relate to the rollercoaster affect with some of your food choices? _____

Which choices come to your mind?

_____

_____

_____

What are some of the feelings associated with these foods?

_____

_____

_____

Were you aware that your food choices might be causing these mood fluctuations? _____

10. GET MOVING

Many people spend a lot of time in the car, sitting at a desk, or on the couch. Does this sound familiar? If it does, you could be putting your health at risk. Sitting is now known as the new smoking; it is that serious! Therefore, it is best to avoid sitting for extended periods.

Cravings for sugar or alcohol are also typical signs that you may need to get moving more. If you are thinking, "it's okay – I go to the gym after work or at my lunch break," then you may be surprised that research shows that this does not completely counteract the effects of a sedentary workday.

Do any type of physical activity every day and find movement or exercise you enjoy. Be creative in squeezing extra activity into your day; even minor moves help. Your muscles will thank you; you will improve circulation and feel less tired.

Energy creates more energy, so when you feel like you are about to fall asleep in the middle of the day, get up and take a short walk. Get some sunlight if possible.

Set a timer, mark your calendar, or use bright post-its to remind yourself to get up. Set a goal to move for at least two minutes every hour. Many of us get entrenched in watching television, surfing the internet, or getting that online project complete that we lose track of time. Creative ideas to make this transition possible could be to invest in a stand-up desk, arrange walking meetings, get some movement on your lunch break, park further from the entrance to stores, or get off one stop sooner from your train or bus stop. Experiment to see how you can easily create change to fit your lifestyle best.

What are three ways you can incorporate exercise into your day?

1. _____

2. _____

3. _____

11. HAVE A PLAN

Whether packing snacks, taking a lunch to work, or dining out, be prepared and have a plan!

Know what you will eat throughout the day; this will help keep you on track. In addition, when we make decisions in advance, there are fewer chances for sabotage during those vulnerable moments. Identify when this weak time is for you and aim to take action for that time frame first.

Scope out healthy resources available. Know where to get a nutritious, quick meal when you did not prepare ahead. Locate nearby restaurants or grocery stores on your route that have salad bars or deli counters. Review restaurant menus in advance. This way, you can decide what is best to order before you are hungry. This is most beneficial when on business or with a group when you may not have much time to review the menu at the table. Think real food when making your choices. Fat + Protein + Fiber.

Mid-afternoon is typical for dips in blood sugar levels and strong sweet cravings. So make a conscious effort to have a cup of naturally sweet tea, trail mix, or an apple with nut butter; all these selections will satisfy that afternoon sweet tooth.

Having a plan will help you avoid the coffee shop to grab a quick pick-me-up; it will also save you time, money, and your health.

Load up on vegetables before you go to that work reception or summer barbeque; you will be less prone to eat tempting junk food mindlessly. Instead, think about choosing the foods that contain the most nutrients when attending parties and potlucks. Consider bringing that healthier dish of quinoa or a mixed green salad, a choice you will eat and that others will enjoy too.

If you want to indulge, consider asking a friend to share your meal when dining out. There are many ways to be a conscious eater and still enjoy life!

When do you think your weakest time of day is? Plan for that time first. _____

If you are on the road often, what ways can you prepare to set yourself up for success?

_____

_____

Who can you call to hold yourself accountable?

_____

_____

*"Sleep is that golden chain that ties
health and our bodies together."*

- THOMAS DEKKER

CHAPTER 3:
SECRETS TO SUCCESSFUL SLEEP

Many people would like to improve their sleep quality. Unfortunately, in America alone, an estimated 50 – 70 million people suffer from sleep disorders or sleep deprivation; we have an epidemic on our hands!

Since the Centers for Disease Control and Prevention published their landmark study in 2013, it has become glaringly obvious the significant ramifications it takes on our health.

It may be easy to dismiss sleep deprivation as something that only causes us to be groggy or feel tired. Nothing could be further from the truth! Sleep affects every aspect of abundant life. Not getting enough can cripple us physically, mentally, emotionally, socially, and professionally.

Adequate sleep decreases cravings for drugs, stimulants, and caffeine. In alcoholics, at least two brain amines-serotonin and norepinephrine levels are significantly lower in the protracted withdrawal period, apparently contributing to the alcoholic's continuing depression, anxiety, tension, and irritability. Brain amines are the substances responsible for transmitting chemical messages from one brain cell to another and regulating various emotional states. The amines usually return to normal activity after several weeks or months of sobriety, although insomnia and nightmares may persist for years. A decrease in serotonin seems to be at least partially responsible for persistent sleep disturbances. Studies have shown a connection between decreases in serotonin, insomnia, and deep (stage IV) sleep disruptions. With **comprehensive nutritional therapy***, however, sleep disturbances are rarely seen after the first weeks of sobriety. * Under the Influence, Dr. James R. Milam*

The above paragraph explains best how good quality sleep is crucial to recovery, not only for alcoholics but for any stressful event and situation life throws our way.

Sleep gives the brain time to rest, restore, and repair. It releases toxins in the brain, regulates mood, enhances the immune system and memory, boosts energy levels, and helps us make smarter decisions.

The big picture here is that good quality sleep brings more creativity, joy, and gratitude.

Many people view sleep as an indulgence; in reality, this is far from the truth. Sleep is a necessity! Adequate sleep controls the body's ability to regulate our metabolism, appetite, stress, brain fog, and forgetfulness. Inadequate sleep increases the desire for carbohydrate cravings, causes weight gain, ages our body, and throws off cortisol levels.

Cortisol is one of the primary stress hormones. High levels create agitation, increased body fat, insomnia, and sugar cravings. Conversely, low cortisol levels are associated with the inability to handle stress, extreme fatigue, low libido, and mood stability. By these symptoms descriptions, you can quickly see how maintaining a balanced cortisol level is necessary.

There are many consequences of too little sleep-defined by six or fewer hours. Over time inflammation increases, and immunity lowers, resulting in insulin resistance. Inadequate sleep raises your chance to experience obesity, diabetes, arthritis, cancer, and heart disease. Mood disorders, depression, and worsening mental illness are commonly linked. We are often left crabby, irritable, and discontented.

Sleep deprivation creates difficulty with making healthy choices like prioritizing recovery programs (such as attending necessary meetings), food (often reaching for unhealthy quick on the go), and not making time to find movement or some type of exercise.

In the 1950s, the average person slept about eight hours; now, the average is six and a half. Teenagers need about nine hours and reportingly get around five hours per night. Adults typically need to sleep seven to nine hours per night, sadly we are falling way below this recommendation as a society, and it is apparent by our health crisis in America.

Modern society has lost touch with their circadian rhythm, our built-in body clock regulating our metabolism and blood pressure. A circadian rhythm is a small group of cells in the brain that sends regulating signals throughout the body at different times of the day. It gives us that baseline time to concentrate and tells us when to sleep. The circadian rhythm is automatically driven by the sun, a 24-hour biological cycle. Any life form that gets energy from the sun has this rhythm. The purpose is to make the most of light and dark time, waking us up at dawn and then sleeping when the sun goes down.

As a society, our body clock started to go out of sync in the 1880s; this came with the invention of Thomas Edison's bright idea, the light bulb. Then, around that time, alarm clocks became popular.

Waking up from alarms can add to your overall stress levels. The sudden noise triggers the body's protective fight or flight response, pumping up your adrenaline levels. In addition, alarming noises increase heart rate and are linked to higher blood pressure.

While alarm clocks might be helpful to get you to work on time, when this activation state persists over days, weeks, and months, it can lead to chronic stress. Stress contributes to high blood pressure, sleep problems, and depression. In addition, your ability to think is so severely affected that it is similar to being drunk.

We all sleep in stages or cycles, each lasting roughly 90 minutes. During each stage, we go through five different stages of sleep, including light sleep, deep sleep (during which the body restores itself and it isn't easy to wake), and REM sleep (where dreams mainly occur).

According to a study published in the Journal of the American Medical Association, scientists had found that when people were woken during deep sleep, this had affected short-term memory, cognitive abilities, and even counting skills.

Thankfully, there is a solution!

The following tips are some simple ways to help you get the sleep your body needs for optimal functioning, which will lead to the energized life you deserve in sobriety.

1. MAINTAIN A CONSISTENT ROUTINE

A routine will start to signal the brain that it is time to get ready for bed. By creating a nightly ritual, noticeable changes in both your health and happiness occur. The routine starts when you wake up! Of course, it can be a little tricky if you get up before the sun rises or during the dark winter months. It is challenging the further you live from the equator, where daylight is significantly shortened in the fall and winter months. An easy solution would be to invest in a happy light to substitute natural daylight. Happy lights are composed of fluorescent bulbs enclosed in a simple box with a plastic screen; they emit a bright, full-spectrum light that safely mimics sunlight without harmful UV rays, reducing melatonin levels and boosting energy.

A dawn simulator is another excellent choice. It gradually brightens the bedroom until it is time for you to wake up. Psychologists at the University of Westminster found that people who woke using a dawn simulator reported feeling more alert and less tired.

Humans, it seems, were never meant to be woken abruptly, in darkness, or by sudden loud noises. Instead, our ancestors woke naturally and gently each day with the rising of the sun. With this in mind, upon awakening, expose yourself to bright light for 5 to 30 minutes-waking the body and rising more naturally; dawn tells the body it is time to get going.

Being organized and prepared for your day is key to maintaining a healthy lifestyle. Keeping a regular meditation practice, recovery meetings, or whatever else needs to get done will ensure better management of your time! Knowing what you will eat and when you will exercise.

Prepare for tomorrow by laying out your clothes and packing food for the following day will reduce morning stress.

Be sure to add fun into your schedule, something that brings you joy and that you look forward to; the promotion of good mood hormones helps us sleep at night.

It is vital to do something relaxing for a minimum of 30 minutes before bedtime. Your bedroom should feel relaxing; avoid sitting in bed working, surfing the internet, or watching television.

As parents, we commonly have sleep routines for our children because it works; ironically, we fail to carry out a sleep routine for ourselves as adults.

How can you create a relaxing routine that promotes sleep and works for your lifestyle?

_____

_____

_____

In what ways can you be better prepared to ease morning stress?

_____

_____

_____

2. REDUCE CAFFEINE INTAKE

It is not rocket science to know that caffeine will keep you up at night; however, most people do not realize that caffeine stays in the body for up to 12 hours. Therefore, it is recommended only to consume caffeine in the early hours of your day. Even small amounts of caffeine found in chocolate, sodas, or decaffeinated coffee can affect your ZZZ's later that night.

Although coffee can have many health benefits, there are several side effects to consider before making coffee a daily habit. Some of the lesser-known facts are increased blood sugar levels, increased sugar, carbohydrate cravings contribute to acid reflux, damage the gut lining, exhaust the adrenals, worsens PMS, and aggravates lumpy breasts. In addition, caffeine impacts the conversion of thyroid hormones, increases inflammation, contributes to poor bone health and osteoporosis, and can cause insomnia and poor sleep.

Be mindful of how much caffeine you are consuming daily.

Caffeine is never a good solution to fatigue; there are many natural alternatives to boost your energy that will set you up for a successful night's sleep.

- A cup of herbal tea in the afternoon is a popular and healthy choice to relax and unwind.
- A glass of water – will assure proper hydration throughout\ the earlier part of the day.
- Healthy protein
- Inhaling peppermint oil for an energy boost during mid-day crashes

For centuries herbal teas have been used around the world as a natural sleep remedy. Always choose caffeine-free.

Valerian tea is often referred to as nature's valium as it is highly effective taken in the evening to help bring about sleep.

The simple act of sipping on a warm cup of herbal tea is also relaxing in and of itself.

Do you feel caffeine is a problem for you? _____

How many cups of caffeine do you currently consume? _____

If you choose to reduce or eliminate your caffeine intake, be aware that some people experience a withdrawal reaction. Common symptoms include headaches, drowsiness, flu-like symptoms, lethargy, irritability, constipation, insomnia, nausea, and vomiting. Consider taking a mild pain reliever such as bromelain or turmeric supplements to get you through the withdrawal period. Extreme caffeine withdrawal symptoms can be prevented or minimized by gradually reducing caffeine intake over time instead of quitting cold turkey. The severity of withdrawal symptoms can last up to nine days.

3. TAKE A SHORT NAP

48% of Americans claim they are sleep deprived, yet only about 24% report taking naps regularly.

Studies have shown that taking a short nap is more effective than using caffeine. An ideal nap would be 20 to 30 minutes; otherwise, sleep inertia (that groggy feeling) happens, bringing you further into the sleep cycle.

If a nap during your day is not a choice you have, there are alternatives to overcome an afternoon energy slump. Taking a short walk in the fresh air, a glass of water, or even a friendly phone call (shown to raise dopamine levels), are all fantastic substitutes.

However, if you find that you cannot fall asleep at bedtime, eliminating even short cat naps may be advantageous.

4. WORKOUT WISELY

Regular exercise (defined as 20-30 minutes of moderate-intensity three times weekly) helps you sleep better; additional workouts per week have been reported to aid in even better sleep.

The latest research is proving the relationship between exercise and sleep is even more profound than we thought. After working out for four months, the Journal of Sleep Medicine reports that insomniacs received a life-changing 85 additional minutes of sleep per night. Sufficient amounts of sleep are better than what any drug can deliver and about the same as what anti-depressants can offer.
Exercise helps you sleep by reducing the number of stress hormones your body releases.

Participate in morning cardio, strength training in the afternoon, and evenings keeping it light with stretches like yoga or tai-chi. Be mindful of finishing vigorous exercise 3-4 hours before bedtime. Post-workout bursts of energy are common and can cause tossing and turning, which may be preventing you from falling asleep.

Tracking your workout activity on an app or paper calendar will better help hold yourself accountable.

Finding workout buddies is another way to ensure you get the activity you need and make exercise more enjoyable.

Who might you enlist to be your workout buddy?

_____

_____

If you are hesitant to get started with a workout routine, what are the excuses you tell yourself?

_____

_____

Make sure to allow your body to recover from each workout-consult with a trainer or doctor. Commit yourself to get started today and prioritize YOU!

5. EAT A LIGHT DINNER

Eating a light dinner ensures the digestive process is nearing completion before you hit the hay. Have you ever had that feeling of food sitting heavily in your stomach while lying in bed trying to fall asleep?

After you eat, it takes about six to eight hours to pass through your stomach and the small intestine. Food then enters your large intestine (colon) for further digestion, absorption of water, and finally, eliminating undigested food. Eating close to bedtime forces your body to work on digesting when it should be resting. To avoid this, eat light at night, aim for completing meals at least 3 hours before bed, eat your most significant portions at breakfast and lunch rather than evening dinners.

Limit beverages up to two hours before bedtime to discourage the need to wake up and go to the bathroom in the middle of the night.
Overconsumption of carbs and sugar causes inflammation, negatively affecting melatonin. Refined grains and sugars raise blood sugar levels. This roller coaster can contribute to waking up throughout the night as hormone levels bounce up and down.

We crave carbs when we are sleep-deprived, so they generally are what we reach for at those midnight kitchen raids. If you must have that snack in the evening, think lean protein + healthy fats.

If you enjoy evening snacks, what are some of your choices?

_____

_____

What types of choices might you pick when you think lean protein and healthy fats?

_____

_____

Tryptophan is an essential amino acid needed for general health and development and for creating serotonin in the body. We naturally produce less melatonin as we age, which may contribute to the onset of sleeping trouble. You might be aware that turkey attributes to making people sleepy. The truth, however, is that lots of other foods contain more tryptophan and do not cause drowsiness. Some foods high in tryptophan that can help raise melatonin levels are bananas, chia seeds, valerian tea, cheese and crackers, tart cherry juice, walnuts, almonds, and seafood.

In a nutshell, be mindful to add anti-inflammatory foods that any mainstream nutrition expert would encourage you to eat. Include lots of fruits and vegetables (go for variety and an array of colors), whole grains, plant-based proteins (like beans and nuts), fatty fish, and fresh herbs and spices.

_____

_____

_____

6. RELAX BEFORE BED

Quiet the mind after you plan for the next day. Consider a warm bath, stretching, meditation, or writing out what you are grateful for.

Studies show gratitude journaling increases happiness. Bring further joy into your life by actively and regularly expressing gratitude. Try practicing being grateful at meals and bedtime. Recruit family members with each person sharing three things they are grateful for; it is a pleasant way to connect and hear all the positives of the day.

If you cannot shut your mind off at night, practice writing stressors in a journal. Write it all out with pen and paper (typing out on computers does not have the same effect).

Curl up with a good book – a fictional novel, magazine, or devotional book. Reading calms the nerves, eliminating excess sound and visual stimulus, precisely the opposite of watching television. Reading a good book before sleep will help you escape to another world without the need for dramatic television shows. Televisions have noises, flashing lights, and distractions, counteracting what we aim to achieve when it is time to wind down for the night.

Dimming or turning off bright lights will help to increase melatonin levels in the body naturally.

If you do not already have a relaxing bedtime routine, what ideas from the above appeal to you that you would consider incorporating?

_____

_____

_____

7. SET REGULAR BEDTIME HOURS

Waking up naturally is far gentler on the body than using an alarm. Teach yourself to wake up on time by priming your body's internal clock. Stick to a regular bedtime routine and tell yourself to wake at a specific time.

Many people rely on alarm clocks to wake up. The very act of setting your bedside alarm tells your brain that it is crucial. We then anticipate the alarm ringing and often reach over to hit the snooze button. Most alarms give an extra nine to ten minutes when hitting the snooze button; because of the duration given, you will reap no benefit in doing so. It takes approximately 60 minutes to reach the critical deep sleep needed for your body and brain waves to slow down and recover from the day.

If you must have an alarm, try downloading a gentler tone like the sound of chimes, or consider a *dawn simulator*.

Another good option is the Sleep-Tracker, which monitors your body's movements and continuously looks for your optimal waking times so it can wake you at just the right moment.

If you awake from a deep sleep using your alarm or feel groggy and disoriented rather than refreshed, you may need more sleep.

If you feel you are not getting the sleep you need, a sleep diary can help better evaluate common patterns or issues you may be experiencing.

To find your natural rhythm, sleep until you wake naturally. Sleep for that amount of time for ten consecutive days. Take the average amount of hours you slept over these ten days, and you will find the number of hours needed per night ideal for you. Continue to re-evaluate how many hours of sleep you need to wake up naturally and refreshed; this commonly changes seasonally. Perhaps you will find that you need seven hours of sleep per night during the spring and summer months versus eight hours in fall and winter.

Sleep apps can be helpful to find your ideal sleep time. Some popular apps are; *relax melodies, sleep cycle, recolor, and sleep time.*

_____

_____

_____

8. SET YOUR BEDROOM UP FOR SUCCESS

The bedroom should be a sacred place; it is where rejuvenation of the body and spirit occurs. Is your bedroom what prevents you from relaxing and sleeping?

Bedrooms are the space we use for sleep and intimacy, not for work or anything else!

Even seemingly innocuous doses of light can stop your melatonin levels from rising; melatonin is essential to induce sleep. Eye masks, blackout shades, and curtains will help shut out the early morning sun, landscape, or streetlights. Earplugs can block out common sleep disrupters like street noise or a snoring partner.

It takes about 2 hours for melatonin to arise and cortisol to come down. Bright screens can lead to alertness. The blue light from televisions, computers, smartphones and other electronics interfere with our natural circadian rhythm, making our body think it is daytime, not nighttime. Therefore, the body's natural process would be more seamless when avoiding electronics altogether, ideally 2 hours before you need to fall asleep. Using evening time to read, journal, or do non-screen activities is ideal.

Work toward a goal of removing televisions or electronics from the bedroom. If this is something you are not ready to do, cover power displays you cannot shut off at the minimum. Use a small piece of electrical or painter's tape to cover the small power lights.

If you feel you need to engage in screen time during evening hours, there are options to ward off interfering blue light effects such as *f.lux*, which can be installed on your computer. This cross-platform computer program will adjust a computer monitor's display color temperature according to location and time of day, offering functional respite for the eyes. In addition, the program is designed to reduce eye strain during nighttime use and reducing the disruption of sleep patterns.

Your home's coolness helps decrease core body temperature, initiating sleepiness. Between 65 – 72 degrees is recommended. Studies show a higher level of sleep quality, ease of falling asleep, and staying asleep longer when the body temperature is a few degrees lower than during daytime hours.

Invest well in a supportive mattress, comfortable pillows, and cozy warm bedding. If you are accustomed to lying on a poor mattress, you are highly susceptible to suffer from muscle soreness along with lung and throat problems. Stiff and unsupportive mattresses put extra pressure on the shoulders, chest, and neck that cause painful joint soreness. Tossing and turning from discomfort for a night or two is tolerable, but successive nights on poor mattresses or pillows that do not feel comfortable can lead to sleep deprivation and more severe health problems.

A weighted blanket, such as *Calm Blanket*, has proven successful in eliminating ongoing sleep issues. The purpose of these blankets is to make you feel as though you are gently hugged or cuddled. The results are a deep touch pressure stimulation that helps promote the production of serotonin and melatonin.

If you allow your pets to sleep with you in your bed, you may want to re-evaluate, as they might be keeping you from the sleep you need.

Can you shut the world out of your bedroom? If not, what simple alterations can you make to your sacred space to promote better sleep?

_____

_____

_____

9. USE BREATHING and MEDITATION TECHNIQUES IN BED

We are continually bombarded with information via television, social media, the internet, friends, and work, often leaving us overwhelmed, stressed, anxious, and with poor sleep!

Meditation before bed slows down brain activity, resulting in deeper, more peaceful sleep. If you already incorporate meditation into your day, try adding a few minutes before bed to see the results for yourself.

A mental body scan meditation can also prove to be highly effective. To perform a body scan, start by laying down in your bed, close your eyes and bring your attention to your toes. Then, working up from your toes, bring your awareness to each body part in turn, your feet, ankles, calves, knees, etc., up to your head. The purpose of a mental body scan is to notice places in your body that you are carrying tension. In addition, this process will distract your mind from thoughts and worries continually floating around in your head that might keep you from relaxing and falling asleep.

Stop here to practice performing a quick body scan. How did it make you feel? Did you experience a sense of ease or more relaxed?

_____

_____

Deep breathing has been demonstrated successful in relaxing the body and mind. A simple technique you can perform while lying in bed is to inhale to four counts through the nose, hold the breath for seven counts, then exhale through the mouth to eight counts. Repeat four times.

If you cannot fall asleep in 30–45 minutes, it is best to get up instead of stressing out about the loss of sleep time. Do some reading, knitting, puzzling, or another calming activity with dimmed lighting. It is vital to do **non-screen** activities. Go back to bed when you are feeling drowsy.

Pick a technique to start practicing and devote time to do it every night for one week. Then, evaluate if it made a difference in a quicker nodding off time. If one technique does not work for you, try another.

Which method appeals to you?

_____

_____

10. ADD ESSENTIAL OILS

Essential oils are the essence of a plant, bringing the power of nature into your home from their beneficial healing properties. Popular scents for sleep include lavender, valerian, neroli, clary sage, chamomile, patchouli.

When used correctly, they have been recognized for centuries to have therapeutic properties and results.

Essential oils help relax the mind and combat insomnia through a calming effect. Depending on the scent applied, the healing effects are limitless, from antibacterial defense to relief of pain and even aiding in emotional therapy.

From a strictly scientific perspective, essential oils are highly effective due to the 50 million smell receptors inside the nasal passageways. These receptors connect directly to the brain's limbic system, which is the area that is responsible for emotions and memories. So, in addition to the medical benefits of essential oils, they make us feel better simply because they smell so lovely!

There are many ways to use essential oils; popular ways to administer them are to rub a few drops on your wrists and gently rub into your neck area; this will allow inhalation through your nose before bed. You can use a diffuser in your bedroom or soak in an Epsom salt bath with approximately 20 drops of your favorite essential oil for a minimum of 20 minutes.

---

11. INCREASE MELATONIN NATURALLY

Melatonin is the sleep hormone that helps regulate your sleep/wake cycle.

If you have ever struggled with sleep issues, you most likely have noticed the general availability of over-the-counter melatonin supplements in drug stores. Melatonin supplements can be helpful; however, they are intended for **short-term use only**. Short term is considered a few days, or up to two weeks of continuous use. In addition, many studies and medical providers caution against the overuse of melatonin supplements. It can disrupt sleep and interfere with the body's ability to produce its natural production of this hormone; not recommended for the long term.

Eating plenty of foods high in tryptophan, which raises melatonin and serotonin levels, is a more natural way for the body to improve sleep quality.

For better sleep, foods to include in your diet regularly are seeds, almonds, walnuts, chicken, turkey, fish, cheese, beans, lentils, and eggs.

Chia seeds are known as a popular superfood loaded with nutrients, including tryptophan. You only need an ounce to enjoy the benefits. A cup of pudding made with banana and chia seeds gives you a double dose of relaxant, setting you up for a great night's sleep. *See the recipe included in the back of this book.*

Did you know that walnuts enhance amino acid that helps produce more melatonin? Walnuts are a natural source of the hormone and, in addition, contain inflammation-fighting omega-three fatty acids. A small handful in the evening is sufficient to reap the effects.

Cheese and crackers are not only satisfying but are also a delicious and filling combination. Stick to whole wheat crackers to reap the benefits of protein and complex carbohydrates and enjoy the sleep-inducing properties thanks to serotonin found in whole grains and tryptophan found in cheese.

Seafood such as shrimp, lobster, cod, tuna, and halibut all have high levels of tryptophan which convert to serotonin, which then help relax and ease stress making it more likely to sleep well.

Certain fruits that contain melatonin can help you fall asleep faster and wake up less often during the night. Tart cherry juice or whole tart cherries are amongst the richest fruit in melatonin. If you cannot drink the juice down straight, mix it with some plain or seltzer water to make it more palatable; the added hydration is a bonus. Simply eating a bowl of tart cherries works; however, the juice is more concentrated. Be sure to watch the sugar content in your chosen products; concentrated juices typically have less sugar.

If you have insomnia, eating foods containing high melatonin levels before bed can increase your sleep duration by one hour over a month. In addition to the foods mentioned above, bananas, pineapple, kiwis, and oranges are also good sources.

---

12. ADD MAGNESIUM

Magnesium is a calming mineral that helps induce sleep. While some studies show an alarming 50% or higher of Americans deficient in magnesium, other studies point to an upward of 75-80%. Ironically, this correlates with the estimated number of people who suffer from sleep deprivation. Magnesium deficiency is a severe problem that can be relatively simple to fix.

There are numerous reasons associated with the high percentage of magnesium deficiencies reported. Unfortunately, the foods that contain high magnesium levels tend to be the ones non-health nuts are not particularly crazy about including in their diet. The fast-food companies and the standard American diet do not typically promote an abundance of dark leafy greens.

The number one reason for mineral deficiencies is that the majority of our soil is depleted of this necessary nutrient, it is primarily caused by poor agricultural practices. Soil depletion has been well-documented since the US Senate made their study back in 1936. Even organically grown vegetables lack minerals – organic farming most typically only addresses the pesticides/chemical issues. The best way to get mineral-rich grown fruits and vegetables is through bio-dynamic produce, local CSA's that practice crop rotation, and soil supplementation through compost and other means. Nutrients can also be enriched when growing a garden yourself, where you can work on the integrity of the soil.

Another contributor to our depletion of minerals is in the meat we consume. Animals need to be raised on good quality pastures with good soil conditions, and this is not happening with approximately 80% of the beef purchased through conventionally raised animals.

The good news is that we can take control of what we put into our bodies.

Focus on foods high in magnesium, healthy fats, fiber, and protein, all of which are low in inflammatory inhibitors. Magnesium is an essential mineral needed for more than 300 biochemical reactions in the body. It maintains normal nerve and muscle function, supports a healthy immune system, and keeps the heartbeat steady, which in turn helps bones to remain strong.

One of the easiest ways to support your body's ability to produce melatonin is to consume more magnesium. Eat many servings of this sleep-inducing nutrient daily. Include dark leafy greens, eggs, bananas, avocado, dark chocolate, nuts and seeds, whole grains, and organic yogurt. Eat for sleep!

Although it is ideal for getting as many of your vitamins and minerals from food, taking a supplement might be the boost you need to get your body functioning correctly. A magnesium supplement one hour before bed can help you sleep better and regulate the hormone melatonin and circadian rhythm. **Always consult with your physician before taking new supplements, have a medical condition, or take medications of any type.**

In what ways might you commit to increasing your magnesium intake?

_____

_____

_____

"Crisis is the greatest blessing for people and nations because crisis brings on progress. He who blames his own failures and difficulties to crisis ... gives more importance to problems than solutions."

- ALBERT EINSTEIN

CHAPTER 4:
STRESS AND ANXIETY MANAGEMENT

Stress is your body's natural response to perceived danger. According to the Mayo Clinic, this is a hardwired physical response that travels throughout the body, and it is simply a reaction to a changing or demanding environment. It is a biological and psychological response experienced when facing a perceived threat or when feeling when the demands are outweighed by our resources to cope successfully. Stress is a built-in protective mechanism. When you experience stress, your brain's hypothalamus prompts your adrenal glands to release hormones such as adrenaline and cortisol.

Research has shown that the immune system may benefit from short bursts of stress that elicit our fight or flight response. When adrenaline and cortisol are released, energy and strength increase and affect the immunity in the body. It physically affects the human body by rapid heart rate and breathing, pale or flushed skin, slowing digestion and trembling. Our system is a delicate balance, and when activated by stress for too long, it changes your brain, damaging organs and the cells in the body. Stress has the power to make us physically sick, and it is one of the greatest killers in society today!

Typical physical symptoms or conditions caused by long-term stress are anxiety and depression. Stress weakens the immune system's ability to fight off colds, flu, and viruses. Stress shrinks the brain, reducing memory, and causing tension headaches or migraines. Stress increases the risk of chronic diseases: stroke, heart attacks, heartburn, irritable bowel syndrome, stomach cramps, and bodily pain are all symptoms related to chronic stress.

There are three levels of stress to be aware of:

Acute stress, which is most common and usually brief. It is often caused by reactive thinking, such as negative thoughts predominating about a situation that has occurred or an upcoming situation or demand in the near future. Example: getting in an argument with a spouse and fixating on it or thinking obsessively about an upcoming presentation. Related short-term consequences are; increased heart rate, elevated blood pressure, sweaty palms, migraines, sleep problems, chest pain, irritability, anxiety, tension, head and stomach aches, gut and bowel problems, heartburn, diarrhea, and constipation.

Episodic stress is frequently experiencing acute episodes. For example, living a life of chaos and crisis, always in a rush or feeling pressured, or taking on too many responsibilities will lead to episodic stress. The effects of this level of stress are emotional, cognitive, and muscular distress; high blood pressure, rapid heart rate, dizziness, migraines, insomnia, chest pain, a compromised immune system, or when confronted with relationship and work problems.

Chronic stress is the most harmful level; if left untreated, it can seriously damage physical health and deteriorate mental health. Common causes of chronic stress may include long-term poverty, repeated abuse, unemployment, poor work environment, or substance abuse. Some habituate to the stress of becoming old and familiar, disastrously leading to suicide, homicide, violence, heart attack, and stroke. A feeling of hopelessness can lead people to give up on seeking solutions.

Anxiety is your body's natural response to stress; it is a feeling of worry or unease. Anxiety is typically about an imminent event or something with an uncertain outcome, whether these situations are real or perceived.

Occasional anxiety is entirely normal. We all experience jitters, nerves, or fear from time to time. Often before important events such as a job interview or public speaking engagement. However, experiencing intense, excessive, or persistent anxiety, fear, or worry can interfere with the quality of your life and the quality of your health.

Persistent and intense feelings of anxiety can be hard to control and hinder your daily activities, job, schoolwork, relationships, and social life. However, managing stress and anxiety is a choice; you can choose to be happy by investigating your issues' root cause to reduce anxiety triggers.

The only difference between someone who is stressed and someone who is not is their choices in response to life situations. So we all have a choice on how we let stress affect us or not affect us.

The good news is that there are simple solutions; merely talking to a supportive friend about your problems or concerns will lighten stress and anxiety.

The following are some proven ways to relax more to reduce your stress naturally.

1. SET BOUNDARIES

Make it a priority to take some time out for yourself. Choose blocks of time to go offline from email, phone, and all other electronics. (e.g., "after 9 p.m. I won't check my email")

Learn to say no in a loving manner and to not over-commit yourself. This includes professional, family, and social obligations. Schedule quiet time for relaxation, meditation, journaling, or reflection. Streamline your must-do activities, set priorities, and execute the most critical tasks first. If you are an overachiever, consider limiting tasks, aiming for three to five items daily. Reduce your to-do list; consider asking for help or delegating. If there is not enough time in your daily schedule to take good care of yourself, something needs to be removed from your calendar.

Review and balance your schedule regularly, including daily and long-term tasks or responsibilities. Finding a work-life balance is crucial; failure to do so can lead to burnout or relapse.

Take responsibility for your choices and make a conscious effort to slow down.

When you have the proper schedule in place, you can relax appropriately. Know that this is an ongoing process as our life's priorities change over time as events and situations continuously shift. Learn to be less rigid and become more flexible to go with the flow.

What part of your life do you feel can use stronger boundaries? (Work, home, social)

_____

_____

What situations are you continuously challenged with that cause you dis-ease?

_____

_____

What ideas can you list as sensible solutions to these challenges?

_____

_____

Talk with another before enacting new boundaries to ensure your intentions are kind and loving.

2. TIME MANAGEMENT

Prioritize your calendar! Recovery, work, family, fun. Find a balance that works for you! Just as there are consequences when our checkbooks are out of balance, there are also consequences when our life is out of balance.

Stop rushing, breathe! Be where you are in the moment.

Give yourself plenty of time to get things done; set your watch or phone calendar if necessary— Reserve appropriate time to prepare for an event or meetings. Add in extra time for your commute, and plan for possible traffic. If you arrive early, this can be an opportunity to take time for self-reflection and to feel your best.

Stop glorifying being busy! Many people do this, whether consciously or subconsciously, thinking it makes them appear more important and boosts their ego. Keep your ego right-sized, move toward slowing down, reducing stress, and find what is essential to you.

Be proactive, not reactive. Identify factors in stressful situations. Let go of what is not working in your life and focus on what is working.

Continuous back-to-back scheduling throughout your day does not allow for the unexpected; often, these tasks take longer than planned.

If you continuously feel you do not have enough hours to find appropriate rest, you may be packing too much into your schedule.

How might you schedule breaks interspersed throughout your day to rev up your focus and clear your mind?

_____

_____

_____

3. KEEP A STRESS JOURNAL

Journaling your stressors is an effective tool to identify or pinpoint your part in any situation. Learn how to handle future emotional disruptions. Each time you feel stressed, note the following:
- Write down the stressful experience.
- What you think may have caused it? And is it true?
- Write down how you felt physically and emotionally (symptoms associated, e.g., a headache, butterflies in the stomach, anger, increased pulse, etc.)
- How well do you feel you handled the event – did your actions help, or did they make things worse?
- Note anything you did that made you feel better.

Journaling provides a quantitative assessment tool for grading, evaluating, sorting, and comparing-helps you analyze your findings to better manage similar situations in the future.

Write out a recent stressful experience to practice writing about this simple exercise. By mastering a method as this, it will become systematic for life situations to come.

_____

_____

_____

Remember that when life is going well, live it, and when it is not, write it!

4. BE MINDFUL

Be present; slow down. Listen and tune into your body. Spend time in the moment, focus on your sensory reception. Reflect on the simple beauty around you, like the air you breathe and the sun on your skin; this will help decrease tension.

If you feel overwhelmed, take a walk, do a quick body scan, or change your focus to a calming activity.

Cease multitasking and focus on one task at a time. A study from Harvard Health Publishing stated multitasking increases the chances of making mistakes and missing important information and cues. In addition, multitaskers are less likely to retain information in the working memory, which hinders problem solving and creativity.

Instead of trying to do several things at once (often none of them well), try task shifting or set-shifting. Wholly and consciously shifting your attention from one task to the next and focusing on the task at hand. Giving your full attention to what you are doing will help you do it better; it increases creativity with fewer mistakes or missed connections. In addition, set or task shifting is a sign of brain fitness and agility.

_____

_____

_____

5. EXERCISE REGULARLY

Physical exercise has enormous benefits for your mental health. Research has shown that regular exercise can reduce the frequency and intensity of anxiety and panic attacks. Fear, anger, numbness, and sadness can negatively affect our physical well-being; our bodies can fight stress better when physically fit. Engaging in an exercise routine will keep the body prepared to cope with and overcome emotions. A lack of movement may trigger anxiety and increase mood imbalances. Exercise is the most potent and underutilized antidepressant. It is free, and it is an easy way to lift your spirits.

Find movement you enjoy ensuring it will have a lasting effect. Do any physical activity every day: dancing, bicycling, walking, hiking, jogging, tai chi, Pilates, or a workout at the gym.

Find ways to add movement throughout your day, perhaps taking a walk around the block, replacing the elevator with the stairs, or parking furthest from a store entrance instead of taking the front row parking spot.

Listening to music or a podcast or make those important phone calls while taking your walks.

We can all manage to fit 10, 20, or 30 minutes into our day, be creative. There is no excuse, we either make our health a priority, or we do not.

Name three activities you are willing to try in the next month.

1. _____

2. _____

3. _____

Where can you easily incorporate exercise in your daily routine?

_____

_____

_____

Take the next step and schedule them into your calendar!

6. MEDITATE

Meditation is a powerful tool that is free to use and has no adverse side effects. Meditation is scientifically proven to mitigate addiction, depression, anxiety, stress, cognitive dysfunction, and eating disorders. It can improve cell health, balance hormone levels, reduce blood pressure, and deepen your life, connecting you to your higher purpose. In addition, research suggests that daily meditation may alter the brain's neural pathways, making you more resilient to stress.

Even if meditation interests you, sitting down with yourself and confronting your thoughts can be intimidating.

Here are some meditation tips to help you get in the zone.

Identify you're why. Why do you want to practice, and how do you want it to make you feel? If you are more precise on your goals, you are more likely to see the benefits.

Make time. No more excuses! Just like you make time to eat, you can take the time to create peace to lessen the impacts of stress on your body and mind.

Start small. Even a few minutes can have a significant impact. So start with a few minutes a day and work your way up to 20-30 minutes if it suits you.

Unplug completely. Do not check texts, emails, news, or TV before meditating, and do not leave your phone volume on near you or turn off notifications. The last thing you want is to cultivate a mind of distraction or anger if you get an instigative email or message. These are significant distractions you are trying to wean yourself from engaging in.

Explore modalities. Maybe you prefer a guided meditation to give you structure, or you like to repeat a mantra in your head. Experiment to find out what works for you. Do not limit yourself to what your friends are doing or what is popular. Many apps are available for your phone or electronic devices; some favorites are Calm, Headspace, Insight Timer, and Ecco dot.

Be a joiner. If you enjoy group settings, consider a group meditation class that may allow you to feel more connected and engaged.

Stick to it. Even if you only choose to practice a few minutes per day, establish a routine. Consistency is critical – a few minutes each day is more effective than an hour per week.

To practice, sit up straight. Close your eyes and focus on your breath, or simply say a positive mantra such as, "I feel at peace." Place your hand on your belly to sync the mantra with your breath. When other thoughts come your way, acknowledge them, and then send them along. You can think about those things later.

Start small; one minute a few times daily!

_____

_____

7. MINDFUL DEEP BREATHING

Most people take short, shallow breaths into their chest; this can make you feel anxious and zap your energy. Focusing on your breath helps you disengage from your thoughts.

Deep breathing counters the effects of stress by slowing the heart rate, lowering blood pressure, and lowers cortisol. In addition, this specific breathing pattern sends a message telling the central nervous system to calm down, perfect for any moment of stress or frustration.

Take a deep breath in, then let it out. You may notice a difference in how you feel already. Your breath is a powerful tool to help ease stress. Some simple breathing exercises can make a big difference when making them part of your routine, especially in intense situations. It works when you work it!

My favorite technique is Dr. Andrew Weil's 4-7-8 breathing; here are the steps:
1. Inhale through your nose to the count of four
2. Hold your breath to the count of seven
3. Exhale loudly through the mouth to the count of eight
4. Repeat for a total of four rounds

Helpful hints:
1. Inhale fully and entirely in the first step. After that, you may find you have to force the air in through your nose – that is okay.
2. Open your mouth and let the air fall out when exhaling. Do not be afraid to make loud noises (commonly sounds like a "hah" sound) as you release the air.
3. You may find that you are slightly dizzy at the end of this exercise – this is perfectly normal and a sign that your body is absorbing the extra oxygen provided. Sit quietly until you feel better, then get up slowly.

There are many different breathing techniques; find one that works for you and is easy to remember for those stressful moments.

Breathe. Know you are strong. You got this—one day at a time.

---

8. PRACTICE YOGA

Yoga is a mind-body practice that combines physical poses, controlled breathing, and meditation or relaxation. Yoga is a great activity, especially if you have diabetes, high blood pressure, high cholesterol, or heart disease. It gives you strength, flexibility, and mind-body awareness, assisting in reducing stress. Specifically, for stress and anxiety, it may help boost levels of serotonin, regulating mood. Regular yoga practice also helps boost endorphins, which contribute to an overall feeling of well-being.

Here are some long-term benefits of practicing yoga:
- **Decreases stress**-yoga is known for its ability to ease stress and promote relaxation.
- **Relieves anxiety**-many people begin practicing yoga as a way to cope with feelings of anxiety.
- **Increases flexibility**-promotes healing and joint strength. Moving and stretching in new ways will help you become more flexible.
- **Builds strength**-many yoga poses require you to bear your body weight in new ways. As a by-product of getting stronger, you can expect to see increased muscle tone.
- **Improves balance**-this is one of the most important benefits as we age. Poses, where you stand on one leg, are great ways to build core strength that keep you upright.
- **Heart health**-helps to relax blood vessels, pumping blood supply throughout the body's tissues.

Almost anyone can do yoga. Any yogic technique used to address physical injury or pain systematically or mental and emotional stress and trauma can be considered yoga therapy and help heal. Exploring different classes at local studios is an excellent way to start and find the modality that suits your current state of health and goals.

Our mind cannot feel calm if our body is out of balance. We store stress in our body; yoga moves that stress out, bringing harmony and mind-body connection to assisting in managing our inner state.

Harmony within positively spills out, affecting our relationships with family, work, and most importantly, with ourselves.

List a few studios near you that you may be willing to look up and try a class:

1. _____

2. _____

3. _____

Who are a couple of friends you might call to recruit to join you?

_____

Make that call and commit today!

9. SCHEDULE FUN TIME

We can reduce stress by programming more relaxing activities into our day. While for many folks increasing exercise burns off the chemical effects of stress and anger, others find relief in quiet pursuits: listening to music, reading a good novel, or even just talking on the phone. Discover which relaxing activities will reduce tension and increase your energy.

Do pleasurable things: reading, walking, or gardening. Watch a movie, go to a museum, whatever you enjoy. Schedule a weekly date with yourself or with a friend to do the things you love.

Make sure to take time to laugh, play and participate in activities that bring you joy. A good belly laugh does not just lighten the load mentally; laughing also lowers cortisol. Cortisol is the stress hormone that boosts endorphins, the brain chemical that helps lift your mood.

What hobbies do you enjoy or have always wanted to explore?

_____

_____

_____

Stop procrastinating and reserve an hour in the coming week to do something fun for yourself!

10. REACH OUT

Seek out social support from your sponsor, sober friends, and family members. Talk to others – preferably face to face, or at least on the phone, avoiding impersonal texting.

Share what is going on. A problem shared is a problem halved. You can get a fresh perspective while keeping your connection active and secure.

Meet new friends by attending recovery meetings regularly. Be sure to join in the fellowship, going to coffee, lunch, and dinners when the opportunity arises. Always accept invitations with resisting making excuses to escape invites; you may lose a chance to gain new friendships.

Help your fellows by listening to someone in need. Make a difference by volunteering. These things help to put our own life into perspective and remind us that we are all connected. Volunteering has its rewards of gaining confidence and skills. The National Citizen Service found that volunteering helps to reduce anxiety and improve confidence. According to studies from the Mayo Clinic, volunteering may help you live longer. Several studies have shown that volunteers with chronic or severe illness experience a decline in pain intensity and depression when serving as peer volunteers for others that also suffer from chronic pain.

Many of us feel detached from the communities that we live in, especially if we are leading fast-paced urban lives. Get connected by being a part of your community and the fellowship of Alcoholics Anonymous.

Explore and list ideas that interest you to get involved in your community.

_____

_____

_____

Commit to learning more about organizations that interest you, explore what opportunities might be available to you.

11. SPEND TIME OUTSIDE

Spending time in the great outdoors can help relieve stress, improve your mood, and boost feelings of happiness and well-being.

Research has shown that a stroll in the woods helps combat depression. It is hard to be sad, mad, or stressed in nature; nature calms our nerves. Think about the times you might have taken a walk in the park; how did you feel?

_____

_____

Being outdoors, or even viewing scenes of natures landscape, reduces anger, fear, and stress and increases pleasant feelings. Exposure to nature not only makes you feel better emotionally, but it also contributes to your physical condition, reducing blood pressure, heart rate, muscle tension, and the production of stress hormones. Research that has been done on hospitals, offices, and schools has found that even a simple plant in a room can have a significant impact on stress and anxiety.

Bright light or a happy light can be an effective treatment for people who suffer from depression (or seasonal depression) and cheer up otherwise healthy folks.
Add a daily short walk to your schedule. Plan to get off the train or bus one stop earlier to walk a bit. If your day consists of meetings indoors, why not schedule a walking meeting outdoors.

To mix things up, consider a bike ride in the park instead of hitting the indoor gym for your cardio or gather your family and friends to enjoy a picnic meal outdoors.

_____

_____

_____

12. EAT REAL FOOD

Often, stress leads to emotional eating, making it hard to resist cravings. Skipping meals invariably leads to a drop in blood sugar levels. A diet high in refined sugar and processed foods leads to crashes, triggering anxiety, irritability, sadness, worry, nervous tension, and stress.

Chronically elevated cortisol levels are a significant factor in stress, which is a substantial factor in weight gain or resistance to weight loss, which increases your appetite, especially to foods high in sugar.

Consuming an anti-inflammatory diet is essential for your overall health, including your mental health. Avoid or limit processed foods, especially foods with a long list of unpronounceable ingredients. These foods lack the nutrients your body needs. Avoid choices that may trigger anxiety; refined sugars, processed vegetable oils, processed junk foods, artificial ingredients and flavorings, gluten, grains, conventional meat products, and caffeine.

There is a solution!

Turn to nutrient-dense, anti-inflammatory, and healing foods for 90% of your meals. Include leafy greens, such as spinach, kale, and Swiss chard; non-starchy vegetables, such as cucumber and celery; herbs and spices, such as turmeric, ginger, rosemary, and cinnamon; low-glycemic index fruits, such as berries and lemon; healthy fats, such as avocados, organic ghee, butter, and coconut oil; clean protein, such as grass-fed beef, pasture-raised poultry, wild-caught fish, wild game, and free-range eggs; and fermented foods, such as kimchi, sauerkraut, and kefir.

Add in many herbs like Reishi mushrooms, lavender, and chamomile.

Minerals such as magnesium and potassium assist the nerves and are naturally found in our vegetables, fruit, and whole grains. All these foods contain high levels of the minerals needed to help stabilize the mood.

Perhaps you have heard the word adaptogen thrown around. Adaptogens help the body naturally adapt to life stressors, especially when combined with a healthy diet and lifestyle. Maca is a powerhouse, along with turmeric, ginseng, holy basil, ashwagandha, plus a host of others. Using them regularly is most effective to combat stressors like a busy schedule, demanding job, or illness. Adaptogens take a few weeks to build up in the body to work correctly, and they absorb best with healthy fats. Because the body cannot produce healthy fats on its own, we need to rely on foods high in Omega-3's like avocados, nuts, fish, olive oil, and coconut oil.

Sneak in protein to every meal. Protein renews and replenishes our cells, stabilizing blood sugar and giving us energy.

STRESS BUSTING FOODS worthy of consuming regularly

Asparagus contains folate, which helps make serotonin and dopamine, the brain chemicals that help regulate mood.
Tip: While available year-round, for the most nutritional benefits, purchase locally in April and May when it is in peak growing season.

Avocados are high in potassium which helps to lower blood pressure and prevent hypertension. They also contain vitamin E, C, and B, which have inflammation-reducing benefits.
Tip: Sale on avocados, and you have more than you can use? Freeze them! Remove from the skin and quarter or mash with a squeeze of lime juice and place in a freezer bag for up to 3 months.

Blueberries can help to reduce cortisol-the hormone released during stress. They are among the most antioxidant-rich fruits available. Antioxidants help to combat the free radicals that can damage cellular structures as well as DNA.
Tip: This superfood is best purchased organic; high pesticide levels are sprayed on conventionally grown crops.

Dark chocolate 70% or darker found improves the mood by increasing serotonin and endorphin (feel-good chemicals) levels in the brain. It also contains polyphenols and flavonoids—two important types of antioxidants.

Tip: Try adding raw cacao powder to your smoothies. Cacao powder is made by cold-pressing un-roasted cocoa beans, which keep the living enzymes in the bean.

Dark leafy greens like spinach, Swiss chard, collards, and kale have high levels of magnesium. Magnesium can help control and limit your body's release of cortisol.

Tip: Save time during the week by rinsing your greens as soon as you come home from the grocery store. Keep refrigerated in an airtight container or freeze to use in smoothies.

Fatty fish like salmon are high in Omega-3 fatty acids, which can help reduce stress and anxiety. These fatty acids are readily available in salmon and lower cortisol levels.

Tip: When choosing fish, look for wild-caught rather than farm-raised.

Green tea, this slimming food, is a great brain booster that enhances mental performance. In addition to its many health attributes, green tea is good for skin and hair as well.

Tip: Take you're used, cooled tea bag, and place it over puffy eyes – it helps constrict blood vessels and reduce swelling.

Oatmeal, a complex carbohydrate, helps your brain produce serotonin which creates a soothing feeling that helps overcome stress. The fiber also helps you feel full longer – a bonus!

Tip: Try switching out white flour for oat flour in your baked goods. You can grind old-fashioned oats yourself to make the flour and save money.

Oranges, which are high in Vitamin C, help strengthen the immune system, which can be compromised under stress. The phytonutrients in this fruit will also help fight inflammation.

Tip: The highest concentration of phytonutrients is found in the orange peel and inner white pulp. Try grating the peel (organic is best) and adding it to sweet and savory dishes.

_____

_____

_____

13. QUALITY SLEEP

Anxiety is your body's natural response to stress. High chronic stress and lack of quality sleep, going to bed late, and waking up early for months or years on end may be what is triggering your anxiety. To reduce stress and anxiety, it is crucial to prioritize good sleep.

Your body needs time to recover from stressful events. Focus and memory are significantly reduced when you do not get enough sleep.

While you sleep, your body restores and repairs the day's damage. When you are tired or stressed, your body will crave energy. Cravings are often a result of being sleep-deprived.

Aim to go to bed 30 minutes earlier than usual, then monitor how you feel the next day.

Keep a consistent sleep schedule by going to bed and waking up at the same time each day, including weekends, to regulate your circadian rhythm.

Journal stressors that keep you up at night before heading to bed. Writing out a nightly gratitude list will help switch your focus to the positives in your life.

_____

_____

_____

14. TAKE A BATH

Hot baths and showers help the blood flow easier, oxygenating your tissues by allowing you to breathe deeper and slower. Therefore, a hot relaxing bath or shower is a good idea after a long stressful day at work. It improves your mood and helps the body and mind be more relaxed to remove stress, kill bacteria, and strengthen immunity.

2-2-20 – two cups Epsom salt, adding minerals; two cups of baking soda, neutralizing acid in urine and removing germs aiding healing; for a 20-minute soak. For more relaxation and further stress reduction, add in about ten drops of essential oils: lavender, rose, chamomile, frankincense to reduce stress, or rosemary to relax muscles.

_____

_____

_____

15. GET A MASSAGE

Studies show that a regular practice of therapeutic massage helps decrease stress, relieve fatigue, reduce anxiety, and increase energy. Although many people perceive massages as a luxury, in reality, it is an excellent preventive treatment.

During a massage, the body produces higher levels of serotonin and dopamine, which cause our mood to improve and our mind to relax. Massages can help ease anxiety and panic disorder symptoms and improve both your perspective and sleep quality.

A review of several studies found that after subjects received massage, their cortisol levels, the hormone that contributes to stress, decreased by an astounding 30%.

No licensed massage therapist is needed! Instead, try doing a hand massage on yourself for instant relaxation that calms a pounding heart.

Roll out the kinks with a foam roller for those hard-to-reach areas. Research shows that foam rolling helps to calm the nervous system. When you use the roller, you can address acupressure points connected to the adrenals. In addition, creating elasticity in the muscles and the fascia can help deepen the breath, which brings your body to a calmer state of being.

Most of us have particular muscles that knot up under stress. It is a vicious cycle: Stress produces adrenaline, which builds muscle tension, which makes more adrenaline, and so on. An excellent way to break the process is to identify your stress target muscles – the ones that get tense under pressure. The most common areas are in the back of the neck, shoulders, and lower or upper back – massage them for a couple of minutes whenever you feel tense.

What part of your body do you hold your stress?

_____

_____

What simple ways might you incorporate to alleviate your muscle tension?

_____

_____

16. POSITIVE ATTITUDE

Reframe your perspective and use positive versus negative self-talk. Flip statements such as, "Nothing goes right for me," "Bad things always happen to me," or "I can't do it," to, "I'm doing my best," "I'll ask for help," or "I can do whatever I put my mind to." Thoughts and worries fuel our perception of events. Energy flows where attention goes! When you focus on the good, more will come your way.

Find the positive, no matter how small, in every situation. Rewire your brain. Your mind will always believe everything you tell it. Feed it hope, trust, and love.

"Whether you think you can or think you can't, you're right."
Henry Ford

"A positive mind finds opportunity in everything, while the negative mind finds faults in everything." Author Unknown

Problems are gifts. Our biggest problem is that we think we should not have problems.
Find a way to use stress and pain to serve you.

_____

_____

_____

17. BE GRATEFUL

Being grateful for your blessings cancels out negative thoughts and worries. An attitude of gratitude can reduce the stress hormone by 23%!

Gratitude increases mental strength. For years, research has shown gratitude not only reduces stress, but it may also play a major role in overcoming trauma. Significant studies have established the fact that by practicing gratitude, we can handle stress better. By merely acknowledging and appreciating the little things in life, we can rewire our brain to deal with the present circumstances and have greater awareness with broader perception.

Science shows us that when a person focuses on gratitude, the brain looks completely different versus what the brain looks like when focusing on anger and hate. At the neurochemical level, feelings of gratitude are associated with an increase in the neural modulation of the prefrontal cortex; this is the part of the brain responsible for managing negative emotions like guilt, shame, and violence. *Tania and Daniel Amen, Amen Clinics.*

Keep a gratitude journal to help you remember all the things that are good in your life. Aim for at least three a day; more is even better. As a result, people who keep a gratitude journal or use verbal expressions for the same are more empathetic and positive-minded by nature.

When you feel stressed, spend a few minutes looking through your notes to remind yourself what matters.

It is not happy people who are thankful; it is thankful people who are happy!

Gratitude turns what we have into enough.

List ten things you are grateful for today.

_____

_____

_____

18. ACCEPT IT.

Acceptance is the answer to all our problems today. *(Page 417 Alcoholics Anonymous)*

When I am disturbed, it is because I find some person, place, thing or situation – some fact of my life unacceptable to me, and I can find no serenity until I accept that person, place, thing, or situation as being exactly the way it is supposed to be at this moment. Nothing, absolutely nothing, happens in God's world by mistake. Until I could accept my alcoholism, I could not stay sober, unless I accept my life completely on life's terms, I cannot be happy.

I need to concentrate not so much on what needs to be changed in the world as on what needs to be changed in me and in my attitudes. Shakespeare said, "All the world's a stage, and all the men and woman merely players." He forgot to mention that I was the chief critic. I was always able to see the flaw in every person, every situation. And I was always glad to point it out because I knew you wanted perfection, just as I did. A.A. and acceptance have taught me that there is a bit of good in the worst of us and a bit of bad in the best of us; that we are all children of God and we each have a right to be here. When I complain about me or about you, I am complaining about God's handiwork. I am saying that I know better than God.

This acceptance passage reminds us that there will be people and events that we cannot change or control.

Let it go! Worry can lead to feelings of high anxiety and can cause physical illness.

Feel it! Do not avoid or deny what is going on. Instead, go within and listen to what your feelings are telling you.

It is impossible to control others and also to have inner peace. So practice forgiveness and letting go. Worrying will never change the outcome.

There are two primary choices in life: accept conditions as they exist or accept the responsibility for changing them. If you cannot do anything about it, then let it go. Do not be a prisoner to things you cannot change.

Take full responsibility for your life and own it. As Tony Robbins states, "Make it part of your job to maximize health. Take the time to identify your bad habits, negative attitudes, and other harmful behaviors that have become second nature." You may find that you may be the one creating some of your stress.

How do you feel or react when you are stressed?

_____

_____

_____

How do you react to stressful situations?

_____

_____

_____

What techniques are you willing to try to reduce your daily stress?

_____

_____

_____

*"This approach is not about acquiring
more self-discipline or willpower. It's about personally discovering
what nourishes you, what feeds you, and ultimately
what makes your life extraordinary."*

- JOSHUA ROSENTHAL.

CHAPTER 5:
PERSONAL TRANSFORMATION
— YOUR ACTION PLAN!

Making life changes can be a difficult task, yet for most people, change is a critical step toward fulfilling potential and achieving goals, both at home and at work. Pain is frequently the motivator that leads us to take action and move forward.

As a society, many people believe there is a quick fix for just about every ailment. In reality, these quick fixes mask problem upon problem. It takes time and persistence to make lasting changes that lead to a life worth living.

Tiny Habits will completely reshape how you think about transformation—making small sustainable actions that maintain considerable impacts in the long run. Tiny habits, or micro-goals, are habits that you are going to introduce into your daily routine. They are called tiny habits because you start with a very tiny thing first, working your way up to your ultimate goal. Over time, this habit stacking is going to help you reach your goals. A habit expert from Stanford University shares his breakthrough method for building habits quickly and easily. *Tiny Habits* by BJ Fogg, Ph.D.

Tiny habits can be achieved by choosing the one thing to put focus on, then the next, and the next, and so on. Avoid making multiple changes at once to ensure that you set yourself up for success. For example, you would pick that one thing like adding in more water, including movement throughout your day, or being more mindful of your food choices. Make that one thing a habit over a time frame of approximately two weeks before adding another change.

Logging of habits will help move you toward identifying factors to produce the goal outcome. Although it is advised to work with another person, someone to hold you accountable, there are some action steps you can begin on your own to identify your behaviors and habits.

Setting yourself up for success:

Purchase a daytime planner with space to write notes to track habits, ideas, goals, victories, record intentions, and schedule obligations. You will easily view at a glance where and how much time you allocate for different tasks. Note: Electronic planners are not ideal for logging and tracking.

- **Physical exercise tracking** – write in the number of minutes of each specific type of exercise you get. For example, 30 (minutes) walk, 45 (minutes) bike, 60 (minutes) yoga, etc., find a way to abbreviate best that you will understand when looking back. Individual goals per week are different for all of us. You will see as you glance at your calendar how much or how little you get movement each week. You will also be able to easily identify when and where you might want to add in or subtract out in your week.
- **Recovery meetings to attend** – the amount of meetings you attend is not the purpose of tracking; it is the accountability to yourself and your emotional sobriety. Scope out ahead the meetings you plan to attend, write them in your calendar, and put a checkmark or a star next to the ones where you showed up.
- **Fun, relaxation, adventures** – this is an area many people do not put enough importance. At the minimum, schedule two social or fun activities each week. Scheduling two will assure that you will, at the minimum, participate in at least one of them.
- **Volunteering (recovery and community service)** includes working with sponsors, sponsees, helping a family member with a chore, or donating your time at a food bank. Volunteering will improve your overall mental health, you will experience greater happiness, and you can expect a healthier and longer life expectancy when you regularly participate.
- **Dining out** – it is essential to track how much you dine out or take out foods from restaurants. We often minimize how much we eat out; you will have an accurate account by writing it down. (If you have thoroughly read the previous pages, you already realize the importance of scaling back meals out).

FOOD DIARY

Keeping a food diary has many benefits, from encouraging weight loss to improving nutrition to pinpointing food intolerances and recognizing emotional issues that doom your efforts. The purpose of keeping a food diary is to keep track of your nutrient intake, not calories. As strange as it may seem, many people do not know what they consume throughout their day, especially after a day or week lapse. Thorough tracking will be helpful to pinpoint any habits that may relate to your health issues. Tracking will also be necesarry to have written out to present to a professional if you chosse to access one.

INSTRUCTIONS:

Make yourself a template with six columns, be sure to leave plenty of space in column three to write in the foods eaten.

DATE - Write the date of each entry.

TIME - Write down, as accurately as possible, the time you eat.

FOODS EATEN - Be sure to include fluids, vitamins, and medications, as well as foods. **Write in the amount of food you eat**, like a bowl of Cheerios® with a cup of milk and banana. Among the measurements, you may use fluid ounce, ounce-weight, cup, gram, teaspoon (jam, butter), slice (bread), tablespoon, gallon, liter, or milliliters. When you list something as a cup (as in coffee or tea), a glass (milk, beer, water, etc.), or a bottle or can, estimate the size of the container or ounces it contained. You may also write in just the quantity of the food when the amount is apparent, like one hamburger, two apples, three cookies, or a serving of McDonald's fries (but write in whether it was a small or large order).

And finally, **write in the contents of foods where appropriate.** For example, instead of writing vegetable soup, write in soup with carrots, vegetable broth, onion, garlic, etc., for foods with multiple ingredients. Do not forget to write down extras, such as toppings, sauces, or condiments— for example, butter, ketchup, or sugar.

FEELINGS, SYMPTOMS - Write in your emotions, as well as energy and physical stress levels, chart your ups and downs during the day. Typical entries might include: sad, depressed, high energy, low energy, groggy, very happy, tired, poor sleep last night, sleepy, runny nose, caught a cold, feeling very irritable, fighting with a partner. Do not limit yourself to just these entries. What is important is that you depict a picture of the ebbs and flows of your day. Try to correlate the entries as closely as possible with the times listed to the left on the diet diary form.

Include **other body changes** that might occur during the day – examples include skin rash, itching, stuffy nose, headache, sore throat, etc. Also, write down the time of day these symptoms occurred.

BOWEL, URINE HABITS, GAS - List your bowel movements, urine voids, and any flatulence (gas). Again, try to correlate these entries with the times. Note any changes or abnormalities in bowel movements or urine, such as constipation, diarrhea, excessive urination, color changes, etc.

MAJOR ACTIVITIES, OTHER SYMPTOMS - List your activity level (i.e., whether you are sedentary or active). Typical listings might include a short walk, working in the garden, running three miles, and sitting in the office all day.

Support from others will increase your success in achieving goals.

- A sponsor leads you through the twelve-step program and helps you handle the emotional aspect of addiction recovery.
- A support group provides a place to share personal experiences and feelings, coping strategies, or firsthand information about diseases or treatments.
- A health coach holds you accountable to reach health and nutritional goals.
- A psychotherapist can assist you in developing a more complete understanding of your psychological issues, and help you work through the healing process.

Each can be fundamental to implementing and sustaining lifestyle and behavioral changes that will contribute to achieving personal wellness goals.

"Make the most of yourself,
for that, is all there is of you."

- EMERSON

CHAPTER 6:
NATURE'S PHARMACY

Our ancestors knew well of the healing power of natural foods and turned to them to combat all sorts of maladies. It is only now, centuries later, that research has begun to confirm the therapeutic benefits of these foods and can be scientifically proven. Many whole foods have proved to work better than synthetic drugs and without adverse side effects.

Vegetables and Fruits by color

The color of different foods can tell you a lot about the nutritional value. This is because each color has various nutrients that the body needs to function healthily. **Therefore, eating a colorful, balanced diet can ensure that you get a wide variety of nutrients**; thus, the term, *Eat the rainbow*.

Red - promotes heart and Urinary health: apples, cherries, bell peppers, tomatoes, radishes.

Orange - promotes a healthy immune system and brain function: sweet potatoes, cantaloupe, carrots, oranges, papaya.

Green - improves digestion and eye health: kale, kiwi, avocado, broccoli, and Brussell sprouts.

Purple - improves cognitive function and combats aging: figs, eggplant, grapes, purple cabbage, and blackberries.

Pale - green and white - contains antioxidants, anti-cancer, antitumor, immune-boosting, and antimicrobial properties: garlic, onions, and leeks.

Yellow-green - benefits our eyes and safeguards our hearts against atherosclerosis: spinach, collard, mustard and turnip greens, yellow corn, peas, and even avocado.

Vegetables

If there is one food group, we can never overeat; it has to be vegetables. These are abundant in vitamins, minerals, fiber, and water. Vegetables help to cleanse and alkalize the body, neutralizing acidity and reducing the toxic load. They are also low in fat and calories (except starchy vegetables such as potatoes, taro, winter squash, and yams). In addition, they are one of the best sources of phytochemicals – potent plant compounds that help protect the body against disease.

Agar-agar - bland and calorie-free seaweed that offers a vegetarian alternative to gelatin. Rich in trace minerals and traditionally used in Japan to help soothe the digestive tract and relieve constipation. It helps to lower raised cholesterol and suppresses the appetite. The primary culinary function of this seaweed is used as a gelling agent.

Artichoke - has a unique healing affinity with the liver, gallbladder, and digestive system. Its main constituent is cynarin, a phytochemical which enhances digestion, especially following meals high in fat. Cynarin reduces nausea, abdominal pain, constipation, and flatulence in people with recurring digestive problems.

Asparagus - helps make serotonin and dopamine, regulating mood. It is considered to be a tonic for the reproductive system with its excellent source of folic acid. Protects against congenital disabilities, cancers, heart disease, and eye problems.

Avocado - helpful during a weight-loss program by satisfying hunger, improving metabolism, and balancing blood sugar levels. Excellent source of vitamin E and healthy monounsaturated fats helps nourish the skin and protect against stroke and cardiovascular disease.

Beet - powerful in its detoxifying capabilities and amazingly effective internal cleanser. They contain betacyanin which help to cleanse the liver, gallbladder, and kidneys—boosting the activity of natural antioxidant enzymes in the body, which protect cells against the dangers of free radical damage—a natural source of sugar, providing energy.

Broccoli - a superfood crammed with a fantastic blend of nutrients. It contains potent anti-cancer compounds which work to inhibit cancer growth. Eat regularly to protect against and fight off infections, high in calcium and magnesium promoting robust bone health; lutein and zeaxanthin, which reduces the risk of eye disease, and vitamin C that fortifies the immune system.

Butternut squash - a great source of energy-sustaining carbohydrates, exceptionally high in beta-carotene, which converts to vitamin A in the body needed for healthy skin and normal immune, digestive, and respiratory tract function. Contain carotenoids, which may significantly lower the risk of lung cancer.

Cabbage - seriously overlooked as a healing food. Contains powerful anti-cancer compounds such as indoles and sulforaphane. Three servings of cruciferous vegetables weekly can lower the risk of prostate, colorectal, and lung cancer. Has a remarkable success in healing stomach and duodenal ulcers within as little as four days. Fermented cabbage supports the digestive tract by promoting the growth of friendly bacteria in the gut.

Carrot - known for its ability to aid night vision, can be used for sweet and savory dishes. One of the richest sources of beta-carotene that converts into vitamin A in the body. This vitamin is required for normal vision, healthy-looking skin, and effective reproductive function, as well as helping the body fight infections such as colds and bronchitis.

Celery - juiced, has a high water concentration, potassium, and naturally occurring sodium, which hydrates the body and restores electrolyte balance. As a result, it reduces stress effects and improves fatigue, rheumatism, and joint pain. In addition, celery is a natural diuretic - found to lower high blood pressure, relax the muscles around arteries, allowing blood vessels to dilate, provide room for blood flow, and lower blood pressure.

Cucumber - the high water and mineral content of cucumber are primarily responsible for its therapeutic cleansing and hydrating effects. Topically relieves various skin afflictions, including puffy eyes and sunburn. Internally reduces inflammation and water retention.

Daikon - this giant white radish cleanses the liver and assists in the digestion of fats. It contains active enzymes and often served raw or grated as a side dish to enhance liver detoxification.

Dulse - full of potassium which helps relieve fluid retention, it is also the most iron-rich edible seaweed, making it an excellent food for combating anemia. In addition, like most sea vegetables, it is high in iodine, which is needed to make thyroid hormones and regulate the thyroid gland.

Eggplant - versatile, protects the brain from aging and keeps infections at bay. It contains many substances, including nasunin, protecting fats in brain cells from free-radical damage, which slows down the aging process of this vital organ. In addition, it has potent healing properties for antiviral, antibacterial, and antifungal to aid the body from infections.

Fennel - a natural diuretic, promotes health in the liver, kidneys, and spleen. Contains phytochemicals, including rutin (strengthening blood capillaries, improving poor circulation), quercetin (inhibits inflammatory conditions such as asthma), kaempferol (reduced risk of heart disease), and anethole (anti-spasmatic, preventing intestinal spasms by people with IBS).

Hijiki - rich in a broad spectrum of minerals, it is a superb bone-builder, containing more calcium than any other sea vegetable, high in fiber which helps to regulate blood sugar levels and elevate cholesterol. If included in the diet just a few times a week, it may prevent osteoporosis and other bone diseases.

Horseradish - used as a medicine in the Middle Ages for its antibacterial, diuretic, and stimulant properties. The kick of aroma is unnoticeable until cut or grated when oils are released. This mustard oil has natural antibiotic properties to treat various ailments, including respiratory tract infections such as coughs and sinus congestion and urinary tract infections. In addition, it stimulates digestion and is an effective diuretic promotes perspiration useful for cold and flu relief.

Jerusalem artichoke - not to be confused with the globe artichoke. Sweet and nutty in flavor, an excellent source of slow-releasing energy. It is an edible tuber that resembles ginger root. Rich in inulin, a type of carbohydrate that does not elevate blood sugar levels, making it a helpful food for people with diabetes. It contains reasonable amounts of iron needed to form red blood cells, while its potassium content provides a mild diuretic effect.

Kombu - highly nutritious sea vegetable used to flavor soups, broths, and stocks. Laden with protein and minerals such as calcium, magnesium, potassium, iodine, and iron. Destroys heavy metal contaminates often found stored in organs and tissues. Due to its excellent nutrient profile and cleansing abilities, it offers relief from rheumatism, arthritis, and high blood pressure.

Leek - are related to garlic and onions. Suitable for low cholesterol and a healthy heart. They lower bad cholesterol (LDL) and raising HDL, the good cholesterol, bringing down high blood pressure – making them excellent for the heart and circulatory system.

Lettuce - helps cleanse the blood and eliminates excess fluid. It contains a natural sedative called lactucarium, which relaxes the nervous system and induces sleep. Its high potassium content is also a mild diuretic, while its chlorophyll detoxes the blood and liver.

Nori - just one dried sheet of this seaweed provides the body with as much vitamin A as three eggs. Used in sushi-making, an excellent source of protein, and helps with growth and tissue repair, its calcium and iron content nourishes the bones and blood. High in beta-carotene, which may help promote skin health, boost the immune system, and slow down eye disease.

Okra - high in fiber, helping to regulate bowel function and encourage the growth of friendly bacteria in the gut. Its primary health attribute is its fiber content which helps stabilize blood sugar levels and lower cholesterol, reducing the risk of heart disease.

Olive - rich in vitamin E and monounsaturated fats, their oil has been found to lower high cholesterol. In addition, it Contains squalene which has heart-protecting properties, oleoeuropein, which lowers high blood pressure which relieves inflammation.

Potato - often shunned for their high carbohydrate content; however, they are only fattening when fried or smothered in butter. They contain B-vitamins needed for metabolism, potassium to regulate the elimination of fluid, and vitamin C, which boost immunity. They also contain flavonoids known for their anti-cancer and anti-inflammatory properties.

Radicchio - praised for its blood-purifying effects, amongst the highest-scoring vegetables in antioxidant activity. Rich in anthocyanins, phytochemicals that help strengthen blood capillaries and inhibit inflammation. Beneficial for circulatory problems such as asthma and arthritis. Contains a mild appetite stimulant that aids digestion and liver function.

Red bell pepper - one of the few foods containing lycopene. A tremendous all-around immunity-booster containing a high water content helps flush out toxins from the body. Packed with vitamin C and beta-carotene, beneficial to ward off colds, infections and fortifies the immune system.

Shiitake mushroom - this highly prized mushroom is both tasty and a potent medicine. Containing lentinan that stimulates the immune system to trigger interferon production, which has antiviral and anti-cancer properties. Japan uses it to treat cancer, AIDS, diabetes, chronic fatigue syndrome, and fibrocystic breast disease.

Spinach - a powerhouse protecting the body from numerous degenerative diseases. May reduce the risk of heart disease, stroke, and several cancers. Rich in lutein, a carotenoid compound that helps guard against eye-related diseases. A superfood for bones, providing calcium, magnesium, and vitamin K.

Sweet potato - best known for its rich concentration of beta-carotene, which is converted into vitamin A in the body. This nutrient plays a vital role in vision, bone growth, reproduction, and keeping the lining of digestive and respiratory tracts healthy. In addition, they are low in fat and loaded with potassium. Furthermore, it contains blood-sugar regulating properties and is considered to be good food for diabetics.

Taro - high in complex carbohydrates and low in fat, makes a tasty change to rice or potatoes, and it is an excellent energy food with a lower glycemic index. It is also a good source of potassium with mild diuretic action.

Tomato - bursting with vitamin C and packed with lycopene, one of the most potent cancer-fighting phytochemicals. A higher intake of lycopene has been associated with a reduced risk of prostate, lung, and stomach cancers. It has also known to protect skin from sun damage.

Wakame - traditionally added to miso soup. It is an excellent source of potassium and may improve heart health by keeping blood pressure in check—an outstanding source of calcium for bone maintenance and magnesium for relieving stress and muscle tension.

Watercress - weight for weight, watercress contains more calcium than milk, more iron than spinach, and as much vitamin C as oranges—excellent food for the bones, blood, and immune system.

Yam - similar to potatoes, they have a low glycemic index providing a sustained form of energy. High in potassium and low in sodium which helps regulate fluid balance.

Fruits

Generally, fruit contains more vitamins than vegetables, whereas vegetable rate higher in mineral stakes. In addition, most fruits are exceptionally cleansing and alkalizing, helping to eliminate toxins from the body and regulate the digestive system by stimulating the movement of the digestive tract and improving the body's ability to absorb nutrients. Fruits are also a fantastic source of enzymes, natural sugars, and cell-protective phytochemicals.

Both fresh and dried fruits are nutrient-rich and an excellent source of minerals. It is advisable to dilute fruit juices to reduce their fruit-sugar content. This will help curb blood sugar fluctuations, lower the calorie count, and reduce the risk of dental caries.

Acai berry - native to the Amazon and one of the healthiest foods on the planet. They hold excellent nutritional content, including protein, monosaturated fats, omega-6, omega-3 essential fatty acids, and many vitamins and minerals. In addition, the fruit's phytochemical content with beta-sitosterol reduces cholesterol.

Apple - "an apple a day keeps the doctor away" could well hold to be true. They may reduce the risk of several common cancers and protect the brain from the damage that causes Alzheimer's and Parkinson's disease conditions. Antioxidant compounds found in the skin responsible for this protection are quercetin, epicatechin, and procyanidin. In addition, they contain a soluble fiber called pectin, which lowers cholesterol levels and regulates digestive function.

Banana - concentrated is an easily digestible carbohydrate low in fat, valued for their instant energy boost. One of the best sources of potassium against high blood pressure and fluid retention. Particularly useful after a bout of diarrhea, which can cause potassium loss. High in tryptophan, an amino acid the body converts into serotonin, improving mood and relaxation.

Blueberry - the number one fruit in protecting cells from free radical damage and aging. Their phytochemicals protect the eyes, skin, and blood vessels. In addition, they have anti-diabetic and cholesterol-lowering properties and may reduce cognitive decline. A good source of vitamin C and contains antibacterial agents.

Cherry - besides helping ease pain and inflammation, naturally occurring melatonin found in cherries may help restore irregular sleep patterns. Certain enzymes found in them offer relief from gout – a form of arthritis pain, osteoarthritis, and rheumatoid arthritis. Proanthocyanins found in them can strengthen blood vessels and slow down the aging process of the skin.

Cranberry - are confirmed to prevent and treat urinary tract infections. Other compounds in this berry are found to inhibit plaque-causing bacteria in the mouth, which causes tooth decay and gum disease. They also promote robust anti-cancer activity and can combat kidney stone formation.

Date - full of natural sweetness without resorting to sugar. An excellent source of potassium, essential for maintaining fluid and electrolyte balance in the body, loaded with fiber which regulates bowel function. The tannin content found provides them with an astringent effect, helpful for intestinal problems such as diarrhea.

Fig - is one of the best sources of calcium vital for bone growth in children and bone density in adults. They contain more fiber than any other dried fruit, aiding satiety and helps balance blood sugar levels. In addition, due to fiber content, they provide a laxative effect beneficial for those who suffer from chronic constipation.

Goji berry - only available in a dried state outside their production regions of China, Tibet, and Mongolia. These berries claim to be one of the world's most potent antiaging foods. A handful in the morning will lift your mood for the entire day, possessing several phytochemicals protecting against eye disease and a powerful antibacterial.

Grape - amazingly is effective at eliminating toxins from the body and cleansing the blood and intestines. They are known to counter liver and kidney disorders. In addition, their antioxidants fight cancer and promote cardiovascular function, including resveratrol found in red grapes. This compound aids in heart health by reducing the risk of blood clots and relaxing blood vessels.

Grapefruit - a healthy weight reducer by boosting the metabolism-stimulating action, which helps burn fat. The pink and red ones get their color from lycopene, a carotenoid with anti-cancer activity. It contains vitamin C and pectin to lower cholesterol and bioflavonoids to strengthen blood capillaries.

Guava - containing more vitamin C than citrus fruit, which helps bolster the immune system. Excellent beta-carotene content promoting healthy eyes and skin; A great source of calcium needed for the skeletal system and traditionally used to treat diarrhea. They have blood sugar lowering properties benefiting people with diabetes.

Kiwi fruit - combat factors that cause heart disease and stroke. Eating 2-3 daily has been found to have an anticlotting effect, which is good news for people with a high risk of heart disease and strokes. Kiwi is an excellent natural alternative to aspirin as a blood-thinning agent. In addition, they act as a mild laxative due to fiber content. They are a rich source of vitamin C and E, beta-carotene, and lutein, boosting eye health.

Lemon - combined with warm water and honey is one of the best natural remedies for soothing a sore throat. Their high vitamin C and natural antiseptic properties make them practical for colds, flu, and other infections. In addition, they stimulate the gallbladder, which in turn aids liver and digestive function. A compound called limonene is responsible for this effect.

Papaya - besides being a superb source of vitamin C and beta-carotene they contain papain, which promotes protein digestion. As a result, papain soothes inflammation, making it beneficial for joint pain such as arthritis and sports injuries. Used topically, it can aid skin sores, and when eaten, treats stomach aches and fungal infections.

Pear - one of the best foods for people with multiple food allergies. The insoluble fiber helps to eliminate cholesterol from the body, which is helpful for those at risk of heart disease. In addition, they regulate digestion and their vitamin C and folate content boost immunity.

Persimmon - contains a broad range of nutrients, including vitamin C, potassium, magnesium, calcium, and fiber, all vital for maintaining a healthy heart and keeping cholesterol levels in check. Good source of beta-carotene and required for the health of skin and night vision.

Pineapple - contains an enzyme that helps digestion of a protein called bromelain. Bromelain works as an anti-inflammatory and is helpful for the treatment of sprains, muscle injuries, and post-operative inflammation by reducing pain and swelling. A good source of manganese, an essential mineral needed for skin, bone, and cartilage formation.

Pomegranate - loaded with an abundance of antioxidants shown to prevent several forms of cancer-protecting the body against free radicals. They not only lower high blood pressure but help fight LDL (bad) cholesterol. In addition, it appears to slow down cartilage deterioration in osteoarthritis, a condition in which joints are worn down over time by wear and tear.

Prune - one of the highest-ranking antioxidant fruits, rich in its phytochemical content, helps neutralize hazards of free radicals in the body, protecting cells and slowing down the aging process. A sweet way of increasing beta-carotene, potassium, iron, and fiber intake. They also contain a natural laxative called diphenylisatin, useful for bowel regularity.

Raspberry - bursting with antioxidants protects against inflammatory diseases, allergies, cardiovascular, age-related cognitive decline, and cancer. High in ellagic acid, thought to lower high cholesterol, reduce risk of heart disease, and promote wound healing.

Tangerine - ward off winter colds and flu with this high in immunity-boosting vitamin C. Excellent source of beta-carotene, important for skin maintenance and immune function. It also contains folic acid, needed to make red blood cells. Phytochemicals that protect the heart and various forms of cancer.

HERBS AND SPICES

Herb or spice, what is the difference? The simplistic answer is an herb comes from the leaves of a plant, while a spice comes from a non-green part, like the seeds or bark.

The use of spices and herbs adds bold flavor to foods which reduces the need for excess salt. Besides adding taste and aroma, herbs and spices boost the nutrient content of all meals. So incorporating to all your meals will not just spice up your meal; it may just save your life!

Basil - is good for the heart, high in antioxidants, and antibacterial properties. Its most significant contribution is in maintaining cardiac health.

Black Pepper - helps the absorption of nutrients and is rich in minerals and dietary fiber. A good source of potassium, manganese, magnesium, copper, and iron. Historically, black pepper has been shown to aid digestion.

Cardamom - helps lower blood pressure, improves breathing, and potentially helps stomach ulcers heal. It promotes digestion, especially fats. It helps prevent heart attacks and stroke and manages bacterial infections.

Cayenne pepper - cayenne and all hot peppers: boost metabolism, increases circulation, and helps reduce appetite that aid in weight loss. It has anti-inflammatory properties excellent for pain relief in arthritis, and may have anti-cancer properties.

Cilantro - detoxifies the body and has potent antioxidant ability due to the presence of a flavonoid called quercetin. It reduces stress and anxiety by controlling blood sugar levels, and possibly reducing your risk of heart disease, preventing the heart walls from thickening.

Coriander - prevent and treat diabetes, well known for maintaining blood glucose level. The presence of antioxidants like vitamin A, riboflavin, niacin, folic acid, vitamin C, vitamin K, calcium, and carotene is incredibly beneficial in the prevention and treatment of osteoporosis-all can cure digestive disorders.

Cinnamon - lowers blood sugar levels with a powerful anti-diabetic effect. Relieves stiffness in muscles and joints due to arthritis. Helps prevent urinary tract infections, tooth decay, and gum disease. Has been shown to kill harmful bacteria such as E. coli.

Cloves - cinnamon on steroids...beneficial against muscle pains and arthritis. It is the highest in antioxidants, has mild anesthetic benefits useful for toothaches, gum pain, and sore throats. In addition, it offers relief from respiratory ailments such as asthma and bronchitis and eliminates parasites, fungi, and bacteria.

Cumin - promotes digestion and a healthy immune system. Traditionally used to reduce inflammation, increase urination, prevent gas, and suppress muscle spasms.

Fenugreek - improves blood sugar level, bowel movement, fights against digestive problems and acid reflux and helps flush out dangerous toxins from the body.

Garlic - an antibacterial that combats sickness, including the common cold, and improves heart health. Shown to stabilize blood pressure and cholesterol levels.

Ginger - can treat nausea from morning, chemotherapy, and seasickness. It also has anti-inflammatory properties, boosts the immune system, and protects against harmful bacteria and fungi, lowering cholesterol levels.

Holy basil - (not to be confused with regular sweet basil or Thai basil). It helps fight infection and boosts immunity, inhibits the growth of a range of bacteria, yeasts, and molds.

Jamaican Allspice - (a mix of cinnamon, juniper, clove, and nutmeg) stimulates digestive juices, helps keep gut and blood sugar healthy.

Marjoram - lowers blood sugar and activates cells that aid digestion, sleep, and relief of stress while improving digestion. In addition, its tea can help in fighting food poison.

Oregano - contains antioxidant properties, one of the most potent and most effective broad-spectrum antibiotics and antifungals. It can help kill candida, yeast infection, and fungal nail infections.

Paprika - loaded with carotenoids promoting healthy vision. Improves cholesterol levels and protects against cardiovascular disease. In addition, it reduces inflammation and is perfect for the treatment of rheumatoid arthritis.

Parsley - is a powerful antioxidant. It supports bone health, contains anti-cancer and heart compounds, and protects eye health. Easy to add to the diet because it is exceptionally versatile and neutral flavor.

Peppermint - relieves IBS pain and headache and reduces nausea, skin conditions, and cold symptoms. It can be an instant stress reliever.

Rosemary - helps prevent and suppress allergies and nasal congestion. Boosts immune system, memory, improves mood and blood circulation, lowers the risk of Alzheimer's and cancer.

Sage - improves brain function and memory. Fights inflammation caused by rheumatoid arthritis, asthma, and hardening of the arteries.

Thyme - natural and effective treatment for chest and respiratory problems, bronchitis, coughs, and congestion. Heals infections quickly from common sore throat to pneumonia, can kill MSRA bacteria.

Turmeric - contains curcumin, a substance with powerful anti-inflammatory properties. Protects against cancers and lowers the rate of Alzheimer's disease.

NUTS AND SEEDS

These food groups provide protein, minerals, and vitamin E, which are especially important for the skin, reproductive organs, and circulatory system. In addition, they are packed with healthy fats associated with lowering high cholesterol, balancing hormones, and reducing inflammation. However, the high-fat content of nuts and seeds means they are calorie-laden, so eat them in moderation.

Almonds - lowers bad cholesterol and the risk of heart disease, rich in magnesium which lessens the chance of heart attack, helps prevent diabetes by stabilizing blood sugar.

Brazil nuts - prized for high levels of selenium; three nuts a day helps with cholesterol and cardiovascular health.

Coconut - know to be one of the most balanced electrolyte sources in nature and an excellent rehydration drink following intense exercise or loss through diarrhea or fever. Packed with medium-chain triglycerides, which help burn fat, improve brain function, and boost metabolism.

Hazelnuts - full of antioxidants, suitable for endothelial function and keeps bad cholesterol from oxidizing.

Macadamias - can improve overall cholesterol with high amounts of monounsaturated fat.

Pecans - high in cancer fighting antioxidants, also associated with favorable cholesterol and triglyceride levels.

Pistachios - improves arterial function and blood flow. They have been shown to help lower the increase in blood sugars after eating high carbohydrate foods like white rice and bread.

Walnuts - good for everything from bone health to cancer prevention to blood sugar control; the main benefit is to our arterial function. They also contain a good dose of omega-3 fats.

Chia - are an excellent source of protein. They are high in tryptophan which helps in the promotion of relaxation and sleep. They are also rich in zinc, copper, thiamin (vitamin B1), niacin (vitamin B3), and iron – all of which are known to help promote healthy hair growth.

Flaxseed - truly a wonder food, from preventing constipation to lowering high blood pressure and balance hormones. They are anti-inflammatory and may benefit conditions such as asthma and arthritis. Promoting heart health by reducing cholesterol, blood pressure, and plaque formation in artery walls, and contain antiviral, antibacterial, and antifungal properties.

Hemp seed - nature's most perfectly balanced source of essential fatty acids and includes omega-3 and omega-6 in an ideal ratio. These fats govern crucial functions of the body, including growth, vitality, and mental well-being. In addition, it may help alleviate eczema and other skin complaints.

Pumpkin seed - exciting news for men, these seeds are often recommended for a remedy against prostate enlargement and protection from prostate cancer. Containing protein, vitamin E, and zinc are needed to heal wounds, maintain growth in children, and boost immunity. They also make an effective dewormer used to treat roundworm, tapeworm, and other intestinal parasites.

Sesame seed - rich in calcium and an excellent choice for nourishing bones and teeth. They are often used to make tahini, a sesame paste that is packed with calcium, magnesium, manganese, protein, and essential fatty acids. In addition, it contains a unique compound called sesamin, shown to inhibit cholesterol absorption from food and prevent the development of high blood pressure.

Healthy Fats

Not all fats are bad. For example, natural organic butter, whole nuts and seeds, nut butter, avocados, wild salmon, and organic eggs are all healthy fats contained in these foods. Include small quantities of these healthy fats daily.

Good Oils, Bad Oils

Cooking oil is one of the most common culinary ingredients you will find in American homes, used in countless dishes, but what exactly does it do?

The primary purpose of cooking oil is to transfer heat to the food that is being cooked quickly. Frying is usually quicker than other cooking methods, such as boiling or roasting. In addition, cooking oil has good tolerance against high temperatures, which means it does not boil or break down right away.

In addition, cooking oil can provide additional flavor, depending on what it is made of, and bring out the fat-soluble nutrients in the other ingredients. When used in baking, it can help with moisture retention and tenderize and leaven the ingredients. Despite these advantages, the main issue with cooking oil (especially vegetable oil) is that when it is heated, it releases trans-fat, free radicals, and toxins that can leach into your food and wreak havoc on your health.

Why You Should Avoid Vegetable Oils

Vegetable oils are one of the unhealthiest oils you can consume. Rich in trans-fat, a synthetic fatty acid that inhibits your body's production of prostacyclin, a factor that keeps your blood flowing smoothly. If your body cannot produce enough prostacyclin, blood clots can form in your arteries, increasing your risk of heart disease.

Aside from endangering your cardiovascular health, trans fat may even impair your memory. According to a study published in *Time Magazine*, participants who consumed high levels of trans fat remembered 11 fewer words compared to those who consumed lower levels.

Much of the reason vegetable oils contain trans-fat is that they are hydrogenated, a process wherein hydrogen gas is forced into the oil at high pressure during manufacturing. Companies use this method to extend the shelf life of their products at the cost of people's health.

Furthermore, vegetable oils produce oxidized cholesterol when heated, increasing thromboxane formation, a factor that clots your blood, and they contain two toxins: cyclic aldehydes and acrylamide. In light of this information, which vegetable oils should you avoid?

Listed below are vegetable oils that can endanger your health:
- **Soybean oil:** This contains plenty of highly processed omega-6 fats. When you use it for cooking food, the increased levels of omega-6 can lead to chronic inflammation.
- **Corn oil:** Like soybean oil, corn oil has exceptionally high amounts of omega-6 compared to omega-3. The ratio is estimated to be around 49:1. Ideally, the ratio should be 1:1 only.
- **Cottonseed oil:** An estimated 93% of cotton in the U.S. is genetically engineered. Consuming oil made from these cotton plants can harm your health in the long run.
- **Canola oil:** You may have seen plenty of advertisements that present canola oil as a safe and healthy cooking ingredient. Unfortunately, this is not true, as canola oil can introduce oxidized cholesterol into your body when consumed.
- **Safflower, Sunflower, and Rapeseed**

Instead of Vegetable Oils, These Are the Healthiest Cooking Oils You Can Use

With the prevalence of hydrogenated cooking oils in the market, what options are left for you? Fortunately, there are many healthy alternatives available, and they are easy to acquire:

- **Coconut Oil:** Touted the best cooking oil you can use for your dietary needs. It has various health benefits; expanded on below.
- **Olive Oil:** This oil contains healthy fatty acids that can help lower your risk of heart disease. In addition, it may help reduce the risk of breast cancer in women. Non-extra-virgin is best for high heat cooking.
- **Grass-fed butter:** Raw, organic butter made from healthy grass-fed cows' milk contains many nutrients, such as vitamins A, D, E, and K2. Furthermore, it has various minerals and antioxidants that can help support your health.
- **Grapeseed oil:** Perfect for high heat cooking and baking without altering food taste. High in healthy omegas with many health benefits. Caution in excessive or overuse in extended periods to side effects that may occur, allergies, headaches, blood pressure fluctuations, and dizziness.
- **Peanut oil:** High in omega-6 like other oils, beneficial to your health with high levels of antioxidants when consumed unheated, and in moderation.
- **Sesame oil:** Properties similar to peanut oil with high content of omega 6. Consume unheated and in small amounts. It may be beneficial for people with diabetes.
- **Walnut Oil:** Valuable benefits when used in small amounts, aiding in weight loss, skin and hair appearance, and boosts liver health. Some side effects can be an upset tummy and low-level blood sugar.
- **Avocado Oil:** Has an extremely high smoke point, at least 400 degrees. Some of the many benefits include high in healthy fats, improves arthritis symptoms, improves nutrient absorption, decreases dryness, and improves hair texture.

Cooking with Coconut Oil:
One of the Best Oils You Can Use

Coconut oil has received plenty of attention, and rightfully so. It is one of the best things you can add to your diet to optimize your health in ways you may have never experienced before. Look at the fantastic benefits it can provide:

- **Cardiovascular Health:** Coconut oil may have a positive effect on your heart health. Researchers discovered that consuming it can help improve your good cholesterol levels while simultaneously lowering bad cholesterol levels. As a result, your risk of heart disease decreases.
- **Energy Boost:** Coconut oil can be a great source of healthy energy, thanks to its medium-chain fatty acids (MCFAs). When consumed, the MCFAs are immediately digested and converted by your liver into energy that you can directly use.
- **Weight Management:** Aside from giving you an energy boost, coconut oil simultaneously stimulates your metabolism to encourage shedding body fat, thus helping you maintain a healthy weight profile.
- **Antimicrobial Properties:** The compounds of coconut oil can help keep your internal organs free from microbes. According to a mice study, subjects fed coconut oil significantly reduced candida albicans, a yeast strain that causes candidiasis or more commonly known as a yeast infection.
- **Oral Health:** Coconut oil can be used for oil pulling, a hygienic practice that uses oil to rinse your mouth. Its antimicrobial properties help pull out and eliminate bacteria and viruses that live in your mouth, along with food debris stuck between your teeth.

A GUIDE TO GRAINS

Grains are the primary source of energy for many people throughout the world. Unrefined grains are rich in slow-releasing carbohydrates that help sustain and fuel the body. They are also rich in fiber that aids digestion.

There are two main types of fiber, soluble and insoluble. Soluble fiber helps stabilize blood sugar levels and lower high cholesterol, while insoluble fiber regulates bowel movements. Grains contain both types.

Amaranth - a nutritious grain that is super-rich in protein, calcium, iron and fiber, and complex carbohydrates. Like quinoa, it is a complete protein along with fiber and complex carbohydrates. High in calcium and contains more iron than most grains. Several studies have shown it can reduce blood pressure and high cholesterol and enhance the immune system.

Barley - this glutinous grain is ideal when eaten in winter months to help warm the body. It contains a slow-releasing carbohydrate and helps stabilize blood sugar levels, thereby preventing energy slumps and sugar cravings. High in B vitamins which help boost energy and combat stress. Barley water is traditionally acclaimed for treating diarrhea, fluid retention, and cystitis.

Brown rice - in its unrefined form, is one of the most nourishing food sources available. When eaten regularly, it may help ease depression due to its B-vitamin and magnesium content – the nutrients needed to calm and strengthen nerves. It also helps stabilize blood sugar levels.

Buckwheat - in spite of its name, is not related to wheat and is suitable for those on wheat or gluten-free diet. Its main asset is its rich source of rutin, a bioflavonoid compound that strengthens weakened blood capillaries, improving sluggish circulation. It also appears to address glucose intolerance by aiding blood-sugar balance.

Cornmeal - this complex carbohydrate grain is rich in iron, fiber, magnesium, phosphorous, and potassium, to name a few. It is gluten-free, and many people use it in the place of wheat. When buying corn, look for labels with whole grain that retain all the nutrition, opposed to the steel ground stripped of nutrition and enriched with nutrients.

Millet - this small grain helps feed the skin, hair, and nails, and free of gluten, it is well tolerated by most people. Alkaline-forming and helps neutralize acidic conditions in the body, such as rheumatism and arthritis. An excellent source of calcium, magnesium, and silica. Suitable for those with celiac disease or other forms of gluten intolerance.

Oats - great for blood sugar maintenance sustained energy and staving off hunger. There is no better breakfast than a bowl of cooked oats. Its soluble fiber, beta-glucan, decreases the glucose and insulin response after eating, making it a beneficial food for people with diabetes. Oats also enhance the immune system and significantly lower LDL (bad) cholesterol levels.

Quinoa - has a superfood status with its exceptional nutritional profile containing all eight amino acids, making it a complete source of protein typically found in meat, fish, eggs, dairy, and soy. Ideal for strict vegetarians or anyone that would like to boost their protein intake, such as athletes. Excellent source of calcium, magnesium, and iron.

The quickest way to prepare grains is to experiment and find what works for you. **REMEMBER:** One cup of dry grains yields 2-4 servings.
1. Measure the grain, check for bugs or unwanted materials, and rinse in cold water using a fine-mesh strainer.
2. Optional: Soak grains for one to eight hours to soften, increase digestibility, and eliminate phytic acid. Drain grains and discard the soaking water.
3. Add grains to the recommended amount of water and bring to a boil.
4. A pinch of sea salt added to grains help the cooking process (except kamut, amaranth, and spelt salt, interfering with their cooking time.

5. Reduce heat, cover, and simmer for the suggested amount of time without stirring during the cooking process.

6. Chew well and enjoy every bite!

Gluten Free Grains:

1 Cup	Water	Cooking Time
Amaranth	3 cups	30 minutes
Brown Rice	2 cups	45-60 minutes
Buckwheat (aka kasha)	1 cup	20-30 minutes
Cornmeal (aka polenta)	3 cups	20 minutes
Millet	2 cups	30 minutes
Oats (whole oats) *	3 cups	45-60 minutes
Oatmeal (rolled oats) *	2 cups	45-60 minutes
Quinoa	2 cups	15-20 minutes
Wild Rice	4 cups	60 minutes

*__Note:__ Questionable due to content, contact, or contamination.

Grains Containing Gluten:

1 Cup	Water	Cooking Time
Barley (pearled)	2-3 cups	60 minutes
Barley (hulled)	2-3 cups	90 minutes
Bulgur (cracked wheat)	2 cups	20 minutes
Couscous	1 cup	5 minutes
Kamut	3 cups	90 minutes
Rye Berries	3 cups	2 hours
Spelt	3 cups	2 hours
Wheat berries	3 cups	60 minutes

Note: All liquid measurements and times are approximate. The cooking length depends on how intense the heat is. It is a good idea, especially for beginners, to lift the lid and check the water level halfway through cooking and toward the end, making sure there is still enough water not to scorch the grains but not stir. Taste the grains to see if they are fully cooked. The texture can be changed by boiling the water before adding the grains; this will keep the grains separated and prevent a mushy consistency.

BEANS AND LEGUMES

Beans and legumes are an excellent way to add high-quality, plant-based protein to your diet, especially when combined with grains, a superb energy food for balanced blood sugar. They are versatile enough that you may never tire of them. They contain a broad spectrum of minerals and a brain nutrient called lecithin. If legumes cause you to bloat, the gassy effects can be avoided by adding a few bay leaves or a strip of kombu seaweed during the cooking process.

Dry beans stay fresh longer when stored in a cool, dark place (rather than on your countertop). Avoid using more than a year old beans, as their nutrient content and digestibility are much lower. In addition, old beans will not soften even with thorough cooking.

Some people have difficulty digesting beans and legumes. As a result, they may develop gas, intestinal problems, irritability, or unclear thinking. Here are a few techniques for preparing and eating legumes that will alleviate most problems.
- Soak beans for several days, changing the water twice daily until a small tail forms on the beans.
- Use a pressure cooker; this also cuts down on cooking time.
- Chew beans thoroughly and know that even small amounts have high nutritional and healing value.
- Avoid giving legumes to children under 18 months because they have not developed the gastric enzymes to digest properly.

- Experiment with your ability to digest beans. Smaller beans like adzuki, lentils, mung beans and peas digest most easily. Pinto, kidney, navy, black-eyed peas, garbanzo, lima, and black beans are harder to digest. White and black soybeans are the most difficult beans to digest.
- Experiment with combinations, ingredients, and seasonings. Legumes combine best with greens or non-starchy vegetables and seaweeds.
- Season with unrefined sea salt, miso, or soy sauce near the end of cooking. If salt is added at the beginning, the beans will not cook thoroughly. Salt is a digestive aid when used correctly.
- Adding fennel or cumin near the end of cooking helps prevent gas.
- Adding kombu or kelp seaweed to the beans helps improve flavor and digestion, adds minerals and nutrients, and speeds up the cooking process.
- Pour a little apple cider, brown rice, or white wine vinegar into the water during the last stages of cooking-softening the beans and breaking down protein chains and indigestible compounds.
- Take enzymes with your meals.

Follow these steps when preparing beans:
1. Check beans for rocks and shriveled or broken pieces, then rinse.
2. Soak for six hours or overnight, with water covering four inches higher than beans. Small and medium-sized beans may require less soaking – about four hours should be enough.
   Note: if you have forgotten to presoak the beans, you can bring them to a boil in ample water to cover. Turn off heat, cover the pot and let stand for one hour.
3. Drain and rinse the beans, discarding the soaking water. Always discard any loose skins before cooking, as this will increase digestibility.
4. Place beans in a heavy pot and add 3 to 4 cups of freshwater.
5. Bring to a full boil and skim off the foam.
6. Add a small piece of kombu seaweed and a few bay leaves or garlic cloves for flavor and better digestibility.
7. Cover and lower the temperature, then simmer for the suggested time. Check beans 30 minutes before the minimum cooking time. When beans are completely cooked, the middle is soft and easy to squeeze.

8. About 10 minutes before the end of cooking time, add one teaspoon of unrefined sea salt.
9. Cook until beans are tender.

1 cup dry beans	Cooking time
Adzuki	45-60 minutes
Anasazi	60-90 minutes
Black (turtle)	60-90 minutes
Black-eyed peas	60 minutes
Cannellini	90-120 minutes
Chickpeas (garbanzos)	120-180 minutes
Cranberry	60-90 minutes
Fava	60-90 minutes
Great northern	90-120 minutes
Kidney	60-90 minutes
Lentils *	30-45 minutes
Lima beans	60-90 minutes
Mung	60 minutes
Navy	60-90 minutes
Pinto	90 minutes
Split peas	45-60 minutes

*Do not require soaking

All times are approximate. Cooking lengths depend on how intense the heat is and how hard the water is. A general rule is that small beans cook approximately 30 minutes, medium beans cook for approximately 60 minutes, and large beans cook for about 90 minutes. Be sure to taste the beans to see if they are fully cooked and tender.

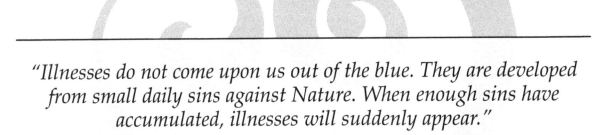

"Illnesses do not come upon us out of the blue. They are developed from small daily sins against Nature. When enough sins have accumulated, illnesses will suddenly appear."

- HIPPOCRATES

CHAPTER 7:
AILMENTS DIRECTORY WHAT TO EAT
The Top 100 Healing Foods by Paula Bartimeus

Anemia: watercress, Jerusalem artichoke, kombu, nori, dulse, quinoa, amaranth, chickpea, lentil, alfalfa, turkey, and blackstrap molasses.

Arthritis: celery, radicchio, olive and olive oil, kombu, cherry, raspberry, goji berry, acai berry, pomegranate, papaya, pineapple, millet, walnut, flaxseed, parsley, turmeric, ginger, salmon, apple cider vinegar, and kuzu.

Asthma: fennel, radicchio, sweet potato, butternut squash, nori, raspberry, acai berry, walnut, flaxseed, mint, and salmon.

Cancer: cucumber, tomato, red pepper, fennel, celery, leek, eggplant, asparagus, artichoke, lettuce, radicchio, spinach, watercress, shiitake mushroom, olive and olive oil, cabbage, broccoli, carrot, beet, Jerusalem artichoke, mooli, potato, sweet potato, yam, butternut squash, kombu, hijiki, apple, grape, prune, blueberry, cranberry, raspberry, goji berry, acai berry, tangerine, grapefruit, lemon, pomegranate, oats, almond, walnut flaxseed, alfalfa, garlic, dill, mustard seed, turmeric, turkey, miso, and dark chocolate.

Candidiasis: garlic, ginger, cinnamon, and live yogurt.

Common colds: tomato, red pepper, eggplant, lettuce, watercress, shiitake mushroom, broccoli, carrot, potato, sweet potato, horseradish, nori, blueberry, raspberry, goji berry, tangerine, grapefruit, lemon, guava, pomegranate, garlic, ginger, cinnamon, kuzu, and honey.

Constipation: artichoke, okra, cabbage, beet, agar-agar, apple, pear, grape, fig, prune, raspberry, acai berry, grapefruit, kiwi fruit, oats, barley, brown rice, millet, quinoa, amaranth, buckwheat, chickpea, lentil, flaxseed, mustard seed, and live yogurt.

Coughs: carrot, horseradish, lemon, sage, ginger, and honey.

Depression (Mild): banana, goji berry, brown rice, almond, walnut, egg, salmon, and dark chocolate.

Diabetes: leek, okra, shiitake mushroom, avocado, Jerusalem artichoke, sweet potato, yam, hijiki, blueberry, guava, oats, barley, brown rice, millet, quinoa, amaranth, buckwheat, chickpea, lentil, cinnamon, turkey, and xylitol.

Diarrhea: banana, date, guava, barley, coconut, live yogurt, kuzu, and carob.

Eye disease: asparagus, spinach, watercress, broccoli, carrot, nori, blueberry, goji berry, kiwi fruit, and eggs.

Fatigue: cucumber, celery, shiitake mushroom, taro, potato, sweet potato, yam, butternut squash, banana, date, prune, oats, barley, brown rice, millet, quinoa, amaranth, buckwheat, chickpea, lentil, coconut, umeboshi plum, dark chocolate, honey, and blackstrap molasses.

Gum inflammation: cranberry, pomegranate, sage, cardamom, live yogurt, and xylitol.

Heart disease: tomato, fennel, celery, leek, asparagus, artichoke, spinach, watercress, okra, shiitake mushroom, avocado, olive and olive oil, carrot, agar-agar, wakame, hijiki, apple, pear, grape, blueberry, raspberry, acai berry, tangerine, grapefruit, pomegranate, kiwi fruit, persimmon, oats, barley, brown rice, millet, quinoa, amaranth, buckwheat, chickpea, lentil, soybean, almond, macadamia nut, walnut, flaxseed, sesame seed, hemp seed, garlic, turmeric, ginger, salmon, carob, and dark chocolate.

High blood pressure: celery, leek, shiitake mushroom, olive and olive oil, potato, kombu, wakame, dulse, banana, grape acai berry, pomegranate, amaranth, buckwheat, flaxseed, sesame seed, hemp seed, parsley, garlic, and salmon.

Indigestion: artichoke, radicchio, taro, horseradish, kombu, papaya, pineapple, mint, ginger, live yogurt, apple cider vinegar, and umeboshi plum.

Influenza: red bell pepper, eggplant, lettuce, watercress, shiitake mushroom, broccoli, horseradish, blueberry, raspberry, goji berry, tangerine, grapefruit, lemon, pomegranate, garlic, ginger, and honey.

Irritable bowel syndrome: fennel, artichoke, okra, brown rice, millet, flaxseed, dill, mint, ginger, cardamom, live yogurt, and kuzu.

Menopause: fennel, soybean, flaxseed, alfalfa, sage, and miso.

Osteoporosis: spinach, watercress, broccoli, kombu, nori, wakame, hijiki, pineapple, quinoa, amaranth, soybean, sesame seed, live yogurt, and miso.

Rheumatism: celery, kombu, cherry, millet, parsley, sage, ginger, and apple cider vinegar.

Skin complaints: cucumber, tomato, avocado, olive and olive oil, carrot, wakame, acai berry, guava, papaya, walnut, flaxseed, pumpkin seed, hemp seed, and salmon.

Under-active thyroid: kombu, nori, wakame, dulse, and hijiki.

Urinary tract infections: horseradish, blueberry, cranberry, raspberry, barley, aduki bean, and garlic.

Water retention: cucumber, celery, asparagus, lettuce, Jerusalem artichoke, taro, potato, sweet potato, yam, horseradish, banana, date, barley, aduki bean, and parsley.

"All food is not created equal.
All calories are not created equal."

- SUSAN BLUM, MD, MPH

CHAPTER 8:
INGREDIENTS TO AVOID
IN PROCESSED FOODS

Want to know what the additives are in your food? Check this list to find out what it is, why to avoid it, and what types of food you will often find it in! This guide does not include absolutely everything but covers the most common ingredients to avoid in processed food. Vani Hari is a food activist who has compiled this list. To keep current and have a helpful resource, go to www.foodbabe.com.

Acesulfame Potassium (Ace K)
What it is: Artificial sweetener.
Why avoid: The Center for Science in Public Interest says to avoid it because safety testing done in the 1970s was inadequate, and some research links it to cancer. See Artificial Sweeteners.
Commonly found in: Diet drinks, protein shakes, powders, fruit cups, yogurts, sugar-free products.

Artificial Flavors
What it is: Synthetic flavor made from proprietary chemicals.
Why avoid: Used to make fake food taste real. Not a single ingredient – each flavor may contain up to 100 ingredients, including synthetic chemicals, solvents, and preservatives such as BHA, propylene glycol, MSG, parabens, and more.
Commonly found in: Cereal, candy, drink mixes, desserts, soft drinks.

Artificial Sweeteners

What it is: Zero-calorie sweeteners such as aspartame and sucralose.

Why avoid: Although they have no calories, artificial sweeteners have contributed to weight gain by encouraging sugar cravings. Research finds they stimulate your appetite, increase sugar cravings, and promote fat storage and weight gain. Researchers from the University of Texas discovered that drinking sodas made with artificial sweeteners that expand your waist girth, a risk factor for type 2 diabetes. When you eat something sweet – even when it has no calories – your brain is tricked into wanting more calories because your body is not getting enough energy (i.e., calories) to be satisfied. So, you keep craving sweets, eating sweets, and gaining weight. Many people never reach their full health potential or weight loss goals because they are constantly being pushed around by these artificial chemical sweeteners that trick the brain and body.

Commonly found in: Anything labeled diet, low calorie, sugar-free, or reduced sugar.

Aspartame (Nutrasweet)

What it is: Artificial sweetener.

Why avoid: Linked to increased risk of brain tumors, lymphomas, leukemia, and heart disease. This study showed that replacing sugar with aspartame simply increased hunger, and the subjects compensated by eating more calories. See Artificial Sweeteners.

Commonly found in: Diet drinks, protein shakes, powders, fruit cups, yogurts, chewing gum, "sugar-free" products.

Azodicarbonamide (aka "yoga mat chemical")

What it is: Dough conditioner.

Why avoid: The World Health Organization has linked it to respiratory issues, allergies, and asthma. When the azodicarbonamide in bread is baked, research links it to tumor development and cancer. In addition, semi carbazide (a carcinogen) and urethane (a suspected carcinogen) can form from azodicarbonamide during baking. This additive is banned in Europe and Australia. The Center for Science In The Public Interest has called on the FDA to ban it in the U.S. as well.

Commonly found in: Sandwich bread, buns, rolls, and other baked goods.

BHA (butylated hydroxyanisole)

What it is: Synthetic preservative.

Why avoid: Shown to be an endocrine disruptor, linked to cancer, causing tumors in animal studies. The International Agency for Research on Cancer classifies BHA as possibly carcinogenic to humans. In addition, it has been deemed a reasonably anticipated human carcinogen by the U.S. Dept. of Health and Human Services, National Toxicology Program. It is also on EWG's Dirty Dozen List of Food Additives to avoid and banned in other countries.

Commonly found in: Sausage, pepperoni, pizza, canned soup, boxed potatoes, potato chips, drink mixes, canned refried beans, spaghetti sauce, chewing gum.

BHT (butylated hydroxytoluene)

What it is: Synthetic preservative.

Why avoid: Shown to affect the signaling from our gut to brain which tells us to stop eating, maybe contributed to overeating and obesity. BHT is an endocrine disruptor that is also linked to cancer in some animal studies. The EWG includes BHT on their Dirty Dozen List of Food Additives to avoid.

Commonly found in: Cereal, packaged nuts, pepperoni, cake mix, granola bars.

Blue 1 (Brilliant Blue)

What it is: Artificial blue dye derived from petroleum.

Why avoid: This is one of the worst artificial colors because it has been shown to cross the blood-brain barrier. According to testimony at an FDA committee meeting, the FDA asked doctors to stop adding Blue #1 to tube feedings because patients were dying, and not from their disease, but from the Blue number 1, which caused refractory hypotension and metabolic acidosis, and also, incidentally, turned their colons bright blue. This dye is also linked to hyperactivity and an increased risk of kidney tumors. In addition, some research suggests it is a potential neurotoxin.

Commonly found in: Candy, drink mixes, soft drinks, chewing gum, toaster pastries, popsicles, marshmallows, fruit snacks.

Calcium Peroxide
What it is: Bleach and dough conditioner.
Why avoid: Its use is a sign that the product is heavily processed. Banned in Europe and China (and some natural food stores like Whole Foods in the U.S.)
Commonly found in: Croutons, sandwich bread, buns, rolls, and other baked goods.

Calcium Propionate
What it is: Mold inhibitor.
Why avoid: Considered a safer preservative, but research published in the Journal of Pediatric Child Health links it to irritability, restlessness, inattention, sleep disturbance in some children, and long-term consumption has been shown to damage the stomach lining and induce ulcers.
Commonly found in: Croutons, sandwich bread, buns, rolls, and other baked goods.

Canola Oil
What it is: Refined cooking oil.
Why avoid: It goes through an insane amount of processing with chemical solvents, steamers, neutralizers, de-waxers, bleach, and deodorizers before it ends up in the bottle. Most often extracted with the neurotoxin hexane – it is bathed in. Some hexane residue can remain in the oil, and the FDA does not require food manufacturers to test for residues. Canola oil is extracted from rapeseed plants that have been bred to have lower levels of toxic erucic acid. Before it was bred this way, it was called Rapeseed Oil and used for industrial purposes because the erucic acid in it caused heart damage in animal studies. It got the fancy new name canola, but it still contains trace amounts of erucic acid (up to 2%, which they consider safe). In 1995 they also began genetically engineering (GMO) rapeseed to be resistant to herbicides, and now almost all canola crops in North America are GMO. Research has also found some trans-fat in canola oil, created during the heavy processing that it goes through. These trans fats are not labeled.
Commonly found in: Boxed mixes, bakery items, desserts, dressings, sauces, frozen meals, crackers, snack foods.

Caramel Color

What it is: Brown food coloring.

Why avoid: The food industry uses four different types of caramel color (E150d) is the most common type used, but the label will only say caramel color. It is created by heating ammonia and sulfites under high pressure, which produces a cancerous substance called 4-methylimidazole (4-MEI). A federal study in 2007 concluded that 4-MEI ingestion led to cancer in mice, and the International Agency for Research on Cancer determined the chemical to be possibly carcinogenic to humans. In 2011, the Center for Science in the Public Interest petitioned the FDA to ban caramel coloring due to safety concerns and cancer risk. Likewise, in 2014, the Consumers Union (the policy and action arm of Consumer Reports) petitioned the FDA to set a federal standard for 4-MEI and in the meantime to require manufacturers to list the type of caramel color they use on their products' ingredient lists and bar them from foods with the word natural in their label. It has no nutritional benefits and is only used cosmetically to improve the appearance of food. It is sometimes added unnecessarily to food and drinks that are naturally brown.

Commonly found in: soft drinks, pancake syrup, coffee shop drinks, cereal, deli meat, soups.

Carrageenan

What it is: Thickener and emulsifier to keep ingredients from separating.

Why avoid: Known to cause digestive problems and intestinal inflammation. In addition, it is contaminated with degraded carrageenan. Tests have found as much as 25% degraded carrageenan in food-grade carrageenan (the kind used in food and drinks). Degraded carrageenan is classified as a possible human carcinogen by the International Agency for Research on Cancer.

Commonly found in: Almond milk, coconut milk, soy milk, dairy-free milk, ice cream, deli meat, cottage cheese, coffee creamers.

Cellulose

What it is: Anti-caking agent and thickener usually made from wood. It is also sometimes used to bulk up foods with fake fiber.

Why avoid: Cellulose is much cheaper to obtain from wood than from vegetables, so the food industry uses wood byproducts to make it. Cellulose can also come from vegetables but will be listed on the label as such and very rarely. Research links consumption of this additive (not naturally occurring) to weight gain, inflammation, and digestive problems.

Commonly found in: Shredded cheese, pizza, spice mixes, pancake syrup, foods labeled as high fiber or added fiber.

Citric Acid

What it is: Preservative and flavor (sour taste).

Why avoid: Although citric acid is naturally found in lemon and other fruits, the additive used in packaged foods-typically derived from a mold made with GMO corn (not from fruit). Frequent consumption and is linked to an increase in tooth decay and also can irritate the gut.

Commonly found in: Juice, bottled iced tea, citrus-flavored sodas, energy drinks, baby food, flavored chips, candy, canned tomatoes.

Corn Oil

What it is: Refined cooking oil.

Why avoid: Goes through an insane amount of processing with chemical solvents, steamers, neutralizers, de-waxers, bleach, and deodorizers before it ends up in the bottle. Most often extracted with the neurotoxin hexane – it is literally bathed in it. Some hexane residue can remain in the oil, and the FDA does not require food manufacturers to test for residues. It comes from GMO corn unless non-GMO Project verified or organic. It is loaded with omega-6 polyunsaturated fatty acids that are unstable when exposed to heat. This instability causes oxidation, a process that generates free radicals. Free radicals are renegade molecules in the body that damage cells, triggering a host of diseases from liver damage to cancer.

Commonly found in: Chips, frozen meals, coated pretzels, cookies, sausages, snack mix, crackers, microwave popcorn, canned soups, and chili.

Corn Syrup
What it is: A heavily processed form of sugar made from corn.
Why avoid: This refined sugar has no nutritional value. It typically is made from GMO corn that produces its own insecticide (unless organic or non-GMO Project verified).
Commonly found in: Sauces, crackers, desserts, pie, pancake syrup.

Cottonseed Oil
What it is: Refined cooking oil.
Why avoid: This oil is made from a byproduct of the industrial waste from the cotton farming industry, not a food crop. Despite being one of the most prevalent GMO crops (designed to produce an insecticide), cotton crops still require an intense application of agricultural chemicals. That is why cotton has been called the World's Dirtiest Crop. Residues from these pesticides can remain in cottonseed oil according to data collected by the FAO/WHO Joint Meetings on Pesticides Residues in Food. To extract the oil the cottonseeds are subjected to intensive chemical refining with toxic hexane, bleach, and deodorizers.
Commonly found in: Fries, fried foods, chips, baked goods.

DATEM (Diacetyl Tartaric Acid Esters of Monoglycerides)
What it is: Dough conditioner that is usually derived from soybean or canola oil (GMO crops).
Why avoid: This ingredient can be a hidden form of deadly trans-fat. See "Monoglycerides."
Commonly found in: Sandwich bread, buns, baked goods, crackers.

Dextrose
What it is: A heavily processed form of sugar, usually made from corn, and used as a filler.
Why avoid: This refined sugar has no nutritional value. It typically is made from GMO corn that produces its own insecticide (unless organic or non-GMO Project verified).
Commonly found in: Chips, artificial sweeteners, frozen meals, cake mix, cookies, cereal, meat sticks.

Dimethylpolysiloxane (silly putty ingredient)

What it is: Defoaming agent.

Why avoid: There have been no significant studies on the safety of dimethylpolysiloxane in food by the FDA or the Food Industry since it was approved in 1998, but the food industry is allowed to use it in anything they want (except milk). Most of the safety studies were conducted or paid for by the chemical companies, and not enough independent research has been done. The FDA allows it to be preserved with formaldehyde, a very toxic substance.

Commonly found in: French fries, deep-fried foods, yogurt, fountain drinks, phase oil (butter substitute used by some restaurants).

Enriched Flour and Bleached Flour

What it is: Heavily processed flour with synthetic vitamins and minerals added.

Why avoid: Flour can be treated with any of the 60 different chemicals approved by the FDA before it ends up on store shelves – including chemical bleach. Industrial processing destroys nutrients, such as Vitamin E and fiber. It has no nutritional value and is essentially dead food, so they enrich it with synthetic vitamins (niacin, reduced iron, thiamine mononitrate, riboflavin, folic acid) that are not from nature. (See Synthetic Vitamins). Wheat has been heavily hybridized to make it easier for the food industry, is believed to be contributing to an increase in celiac disease, and is often sprayed directly with Monsanto's Roundup herbicide.

Commonly found in: Sandwich bread, buns, rolls, and other baked goods.

Erythritol

What it is: Sugar alcohol and low-calorie sweetener.

Why avoid: It can wreak havoc on healthy gut bacteria, which can lead to a whole host of diseases, and if you are trying to lose weight or stay slim, keeping your gut healthy is vital! Erythritol is also known to cause diarrhea, stomach upset, headache when consumed in average amounts, is a powerful insecticide, and can also increase appetite just like artificial sweeteners do, so you will end up eating more food. Research by Cornell University shows that the body metabolizes erythritol and associates high levels of erythritol in the blood to weight gain, which has spawned more studies. Although this is a naturally occurring sugar found in fruit, food manufacturers do not use the natural stuff. Instead, they usually start with GMO corn (unless organic or non-GMO verified) and then put it through a complex fermentation process to come up with chemically pure erythritol. **Commonly found in:** Stevia products, diet drinks, yogurt, pudding cups.

Fructose or Fructose Syrup

See HFCS-90

Gellan Gum, Locust Bean Gum, and Guar Gum

What it is: Thickener.

Why avoid: These ingredients are known to cause stomach issues like bloating and gas in people who have sensitive digestive systems.

Commonly found in: Almond milk, coconut milk, soy milk, non-dairy milk and creamers, ice cream, cottage cheese.

High Fructose Corn Syrup (HFCS)

What it is: Heavily processed sweetener made from cornstarch, contains more fructose than regular corn syrup.

Why avoid: This sweetener increases appetite, the risk of weight gain, type 2 diabetes, heart disease, cancer, and dementia. HFCS significantly contributes to type 2 diabetes in children. One study also found it can be contaminated with toxic mercury.

Commonly found in: Soft drinks, pancake syrup, BBQ sauce, ketchup, cookies, bread, buns, frosting, pies.

HFCS-90 (Fructose or Fructose Syrup)

What it is: Heavily processed sweetener made from cornstarch-contains more fructose than high fructose corn syrup. Regular HFCS contains up to 55% fructose, whereas HFCS-90 has 90% fructose by weight-nine times more fructose than the average fruit.

Why avoid: An overload of fructose in the diet is associated with obesity and cardiovascular disease. HFCS-90; derived from corn starch, which is likely GMO. Some companies say that fructose is natural and comes from fruit, but this processed additive is typically derived from GMO corn. When HFCS-90 is used, the ingredient label will not indicate that high fructose corn syrup is an ingredient; instead, it is deceptively labeled as fructose or fructose syrup without any reference to high fructose corn syrup.

Commonly found in: Yogurt, cereal, granola bars, potato chips.

Hydrolyzed Protein (any type of hydrolyzed protein)

See Monosodium Glutamate.

Maltodextrin

What it is: Heavily processed starch used as a filler, thickener, preservative, and sweetener.

Why avoid: It has been shown to negatively affect gut bacteria, putting you at greater risk of disease. It has no nutritional value (not real food) and can be used as a filler to artificially increase the volume of processed foods, so this indicates heavily processed food. It is typically derived from GMO corn (unless organic or non-GMO Project verified). It is also a hidden form of MSG.

Commonly found in: Potato chips, mac n' cheese, frozen meals, powder drink mixes, pudding.

Monoglycerides and Diglycerides (mono- and diglycerides)

What it is: Emulsifier, which helps keep ingredients from separating.

Why avoid: It is made from oil byproducts, including partially hydrogenated canola and soybean oils – which contain artificial trans-fat, making this additive a hidden source of trans fat in our food. Even in foods labeled as zero grams of trans fat, it is permitted because it is categorized as an emulsifier (not a lipid) by the FDA. The consumption of artificial trans-fat is strongly correlated with an increased risk of type 2 diabetes and heart disease. The CDC has linked it to at least 20,000 heart attacks per year, and the Institute of Medicine says trans fats have no known health benefits and there is no safe level to eat.

Commonly found in: Ice cream sandwiches, low-fat ice cream, frozen yogurt, peanut butter, margarine, non-dairy creamer, tortillas, bread.

Monosodium Glutamate (MSG)

What it is: Artificial flavor enhancer.

Why avoid: Purely used to increase food cravings and irresistibility, so you eat more than you should. It is linked to headaches, obesity, depression, and mental disorders. It is also an excitotoxin (excites brain cells to death) associated with neurodegenerative diseases. Besides the additive monosodium glutamate (MSG), the food industry sneaks in other additives – such as yeast extract and hydrolyzed proteins – containing free glutamic acid, which is the main component of MSG.

Commonly found in: Frozen meals, chips, dressings, soups, rice, and pasta mixes.

Natural Flavors

What it is: Flavors are made from a proprietary mixture of chemicals derived from anything in nature.

Why avoid: The only difference between natural and artificial flavors is that natural flavors are derived from things found in nature. Natural flavors are used to make fake food taste real. Every flavor may contain up to 100 ingredients, including synthetic chemicals such as the solvent propylene glycol or the preservative BHA and GMO-derived ingredients (unless organic or non-GMO Project verified). Flavors can also include excitotoxins like MSG that cause your taste buds to experience irresistibility when it comes to food. See MSG.

Commonly found in: Almost all processed food.

Neotame

What it is: Artificial sweetener.

Why avoid: Relatively new and rarely used, some health experts warn that it is more harmful to our health than aspartame – a neurotoxin – but its safety is still up in the air. Often used along with other artificial sweeteners. See Artificial Sweeteners.

Commonly found in: Diet juice, yogurt, chewing gum, diet soda, orange drink, drink mixes.

Propylparaben or Methylparaben

What it is: Synthetic preservatives.

Why avoid: Parabens are endocrine-disrupting chemicals linked to breast cancer and reproductive problems. EWG includes propylparaben on their Dirty Dozen list of top food additives to avoid.

Commonly found in: Snack cakes, desserts, frosting, tortillas.

Partially Hydrogenated Oils (Artificial Trans Fat)

What it is: Oil that is solidified with chemical processing. Typically made with GMO soybean, cottonseed, or canola oil.

Why avoid: Strongly correlated with an increased risk of type 2 diabetes and heart disease. The CDC has linked it to at least 20,000 heart attacks per year, and the Institute of Medicine says trans fats have no known health benefits and there is no safe level to eat. The FDA requires all food manufacturers to remove partially hydrogenated oils by June 2018, but food companies can still petition the FDA for a special permit to continue using it. The FDA allows any product is labeled zero grams of Trans Fat to contain up to 0.5 grams of trans fat per serving, plus other additives that contain trans fat. See Monoglycerides.

Commonly found in: Frosting, baked goods, non-dairy creamers, cookies, crackers.

Propyl Gallate

What it is: Synthetic preservative.

Why avoid: Linked to increased risk of tumors and endocrine disruption and is on EWG's list of additives to avoid.

Commonly found in: Sausage, pizza, stuffing mix.

Red 3 (Erythrosine)

What it is: Artificial red dye derived from petroleum.

Why avoid: Recognized as an animal carcinogen, it was banned from cosmetics in 1990, yet the FDA still permits it in food.

Commonly found in: Strawberry milk, baked goods, maraschino cherries, candy, sausage casings.

Red 40 (Allura Red)

What it is: Artificial red dye derived from petroleum.

Why avoid: The most popular artificial color used in the U.S., linked to hyperactivity in children. Europe requires any food containing this dye to carry the warning label, May Have an Adverse Effect on Activity and Attention in Children. This is why many food companies use natural colors in Europe instead. Controversial research suggests this dye can accelerate the appearance of tumors. It has no nutritional benefits and is only used cosmetically to improve the appearance of food.

Commonly found in: soft drinks, candy, cake, frosting, cookies, fruit cups, cherry filling, popsicles, toaster pastries, cereal bars, cereals, ice cream, yogurt, drink mixes.

Sodium Benzoate or Potassium Benzoate

What it is: Synthetic preservatives.

Why avoid: When combined with either ascorbic acid (vitamin C) or erythorbic acid, it produces benzene, a known carcinogen.

Commonly found in: soft drinks, pickles, syrups, sauces, salad dressing.

Sodium Nitrate and Sodium Nitrite

What it is: Synthetic preservatives.

Why avoid: Linked to increased risk of cancer.

Commonly found in: Deli meat, ham, sausage, hot dogs, bacon, jerky, meat snacks.

Sodium Phosphate

What it is: Preservative.

The EWG warns that sodium phosphate is a top additive to avoid. Why avoid: It is so commonly used that you likely eat it daily if you eat processed food. When you eat phosphate additives often, it can lead to excessive phosphate levels in the blood and puts you at risk of chronic kidney disease, increased mortality, heart disease, and accelerated aging.

Commonly found in: cooked chicken, pudding, gelatin, mac n' cheese, frozen desserts, frozen meals, soup, deli meat, imitation cheese slices.

Soybean Oil (Vegetable Oil)

What it is: Refined cooking oil.

Why avoid: One of the unhealthiest oils out there, which increases the risk of obesity, inflammation, cardiovascular disease, cancer, and autoimmune diseases. It is almost always made from GMO soybeans (unless organic or Non-GMO Project verified). When researchers tested GMO soybeans, they found high levels of residues from the herbicide glyphosate (Monsanto's Roundup) compared to non-GMO soybeans. Glyphosate was deemed a probable carcinogen by the World Health Organization (WHO) and linked to kidney disease, congenital disabilities, and autism. The soybeans are typically subjected to intensive chemical refining with toxic hexane, bleach, and deodorizers to extract the oil.

Commonly found in: Vegetable oil, salad dressing, crackers, cookies, baked goods, trail mix, potato chips, frozen meals, frozen desserts, buns, soup, sauces.

Soy Protein Isolate

What it is: Heavily processed protein supplement made from soy flour that has fiber, fat, and nutrients removed.

Why avoid: Soy can cause hormonal disruptions because it has estrogen-mimicking properties. Soy also has an abundance of phytic acid that leaches calcium and other vital minerals from your body. The soy protein is usually extracted with the neurotoxin hexane (and the final product may contain residues of hexane). It is also almost always made from GMO soybeans (unless organic or non-GMO Project verified). When researchers tested GMO soybeans, they found high levels of residues from the herbicide glyphosate (Monsanto's Roundup) compared to non-GMO soybeans. Glyphosate was deemed a probable carcinogen by the World Health Organization (WHO) and linked to kidney disease, congenital disabilities, and autism.

Commonly found in: Protein powder, protein shakes, protein bars, veggie burgers, veggie dogs, soup, frozen meals.

Sucralose (Splenda)

What it is: Artificial sweetener made by chlorinating sugar.

Why avoid: Independent animal research links it to leukemia and other blood cancers. It has also been shown that artificial sweeteners are doing little to help people lose weight and are actually linked to weight gain. See Artificial Sweeteners.

Commonly found in: Chewing gum, diet sodas, drinks, iced tea, yogurt, pudding, fruit cups.

Stevia Extract (rebaudioside A or reb A)

What it is: Low-calorie sweetener.

Why avoid: This is not the same as the whole stevia leaf that you can grow in your backyard. The extract is highly processed using a patentable chemical-laden process that includes about 40 steps to process the extract from the leaf, relying on chemicals like acetone, methanol, ethanol, acetonitrile, and isopropanol. Some of these chemicals are known carcinogens (substances that cause cancer). Most stevia formulations on the market also contain natural flavors and either erythritol or dextrose. Look for Whole Leaf Stevia or an extract that contains no additional additives instead.

Commonly found in: Soft drinks, coconut water, kombucha, bottled tea, protein drinks, protein bars, juice, yogurt.

Synthetic Vitamins

What they are: Lab-created vitamins made from various sources like coal tar, petroleum or GMOs.

Examples: Vitamin A Palmitate, Thiamine (vitamin B1), Riboflavin (vitamin B2), Ascorbic Acid (vitamin C), Folic Acid.

Why avoid: These vitamins differ from their natural counterparts; thus, they are not believed to be absorbed by your body and naturally present vitamins you get from whole food. These are often found in foods labeled Enriched or Fortified. Unfortunately, some of these fortified foods have been found to have dangerously high levels of synthetic vitamins and minerals – especially for kids.

Commonly found in: Cereal, bread, snack bars, protein drinks, meal replacements, supplements.

Tapioca Starch

What it is: Starch is often used to replace wheat in gluten-free foods.

Why avoid: Tapioca starch can be hard to avoid completely on a gluten-free diet, but it is something to be aware of and limit. It is extremely high in carbohydrates but hardly contains fiber, fat, protein, vitamins, or minerals. It just supplies empty calories that can spike blood sugar more than refined sugar does.

Commonly found in: Gluten-free bread, gluten-free tortillas, gluten-free baked goods, gluten-free crackers.

TBHQ (tert-butylhydroquinone)

What it is: Synthetic preservative.

Why avoid: It has been linked to vision disturbances, liver enlargement, childhood behavioral problems, stomach cancer, and most recently, to the rise in food allergies. Research shows that TBHQ negatively affects T-cells in the body to promote allergies to tree nuts, milk, eggs, wheat, and shellfish. It is also banned for use in food in other countries, including Japan, and is on the Center for Science in The Public Interest's list as one of the worst food additives to be avoided. This ingredient is not always on the label.

Often found in: crackers, cookies, microwave popcorn, peanut butter chocolates, pastries, biscuits, frozen pizza.

Titanium Dioxide

What it is: Food color used to brighten and whiten.

Why avoid: Microscopic particles (nanoparticles) of titanium dioxide are sometimes used to make white foods even whiter and brighter, however, it is not always labeled. According to Friends of the Earth, there has been "a tenfold increase in unregulated, unlabeled "nanofood" products on the American market since 2008… made by major companies including Kraft, General Mills, Hershey, Nestle, Mars, Unilever, Smucker's, and Albertsons. But due to a lack of labeling and disclosure, a far greater number of food products with undisclosed nanomaterials are likely currently on the market." Nanoparticles have been shown to carry risks to human health and the environment, and nanoparticles of titanium dioxide are specifically linked to cancer, gastrointestinal inflammation, and changes to digestive cell structure. As put by the Natural Resources Defense Council, "Nanoparticles…are also more toxic than their normal-sized counterparts. Because they are so small, nanoparticles are extremely mobile. Once inside the body, they seem to have unlimited access to all tissues and organs, including the brain and likely also the fetal circulation, and may cause cell damage that we do not yet understand."

Commonly found in: Yogurt, cottage cheese, powdered sugar, candy, chewing gum, pudding, drink mixes, marshmallows, mayonnaise.

Vanillin
What it is: Artificial flavor (imitation vanilla) typically made from petrochemicals and wood pulp.
Why avoid: It is fake food, and as an artificial flavor, it tricks your brain into believing that you are eating real vanilla. It also does not contain all of the antioxidants found in real vanilla extract good for the body.
Commonly found in: Milkshakes, ice cream, yogurt, protein shakes, candy.

Yeast Extract (autolyzed yeast extract)
See Monosodium Glutamate

Yellow #5 (Tartrazine and Yellow #6 Sunset Yellow)
What it is: Artificial yellow dyes derived from petroleum.
Why avoid: Linked to several health issues, including allergies and hyperactivity in children. Europe requires any food containing dyes to carry the warning label, May Have an Adverse Effect on Activity and Attention in Children. This is why many food companies use natural colors in Europe instead. These dyes have been found to be contaminated with carcinogens, such as benzidine. They have no nutritional benefits and are only used cosmetically to improve the appearance of food.
Commonly found in: Candy, fruit snacks, cereals, mac n' cheese, chips, pickles.

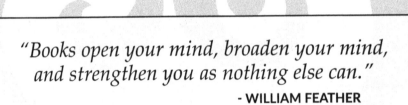

"Books open your mind, broaden your mind, and strengthen you as nothing else can."

- WILLIAM FEATHER

CHAPTER 9:
RECOMMENDED RESOURCES

Books

Alcoholics Anonymous – The story of how many thousands of men and women have recovered from alcoholism.

A Mind of Your Own: The Truth about Depression and How Women Can Heal Their Bodies to Reclaim Their Lives, Kelly Brogan, MD – Depression is not a disease, but a symptom. one in four women start their day with antidepressants, the panacea for grief, irritability, panic attacks, insomnia, PMS, and stress. The best way to heal the mind is to heal the whole body. It shatters the mythology conventional medicine has built around the causes and treatment of depression. It is not simply a chemical imbalance but a lifestyle crisis that demands a reset from blood sugar to gut health to thyroid function with inflammation at the root. Includes powerful dietary interventions, targeted nutrient support, detoxification, sleep, and stress reframing techniques to alleviate these symptoms.

Breaking the Food Seduction, Dr. Neal Bernard – If sweets and high-fat foods are sabotaging your efforts to lose weight and get healthy, this is a solution to conquer your food addictions. Backed up by scientific research, Bernard explains that your biochemistry, not your lack of willpower, is the problem. Addressing simple dietary and lifestyle changes that can break the stubborn cycle of cravings and free you to choose healthy, tasty foods that help you lose weight, lower cholesterol, and improve your overall health.

Change Your Brain, Change your Body, Dr. Daniel Amen – The breakthrough program for conquering anxiety, depression, obsessiveness, lack of focus, anger, and memory. Amen is a self-help guru and psychiatrist, founded clinics in 1989, with eight clinics around the country. A group of mental and physical health clinics that work on the treatment of mood and behavioral disorders.

Dr. Neal Bernard Program for Reversing Diabetes – A nutritional approach to diabetes that dramatically alters how we think about treating the disease. Most health professionals consider diabetes a one-way street; once you have developed it, you are stuck with it. You can anticipate one complication after another from worsening of eyesight, nerve symptoms, heart and kidney problems. The National Institute for Health has shown it does not have to be that way. Following a specific diet, you can control blood sugar three times more effectively than with the American Diabetes Association diet. Beyond this, improve the body's ability to respond to insulin, reversing the disease.

Food Fix, Mark Hyman, MD – explains how our food and agriculture policies are unfairly influenced by money and lobbyists that drive our biggest global crisis: the spread of obesity and food-related chronic disease, climate change, poverty, violence, educational achievement gaps, social injustice, and more.

Mad Cowboy, Howard Lyman – a fourth generation rancher that produced dairy and meat commodities and is now a vegetarian. Kicked off the infamous lawsuit between Oprah and the cattleman, Mad Cowboy, in an impassionate account of the unsafe practices of the cattle and dairy industries. Howard's testimony revealed the deadly impact of the livestock industry on our well-being.

Natural Cures Handbook, Prevention Magazine – Remedies for 60+ common ailments

Sugar, Salt, Fat, Michael Moss – how corporate food manufacturers have come to rely on salt, sugar, and fat as the mainstays of processed and prepackaged food. The food industry in the US has become intensely dependent on these harmful ingredients to achieve its massive profits. As a result, they contribute to public health problems and the rising incidence of diabetes and obesity. As a result, food executives have sought to manipulate consumption and drive up revenue at the expense of their consumers' health. To maintain an advantage against rival companies, food manufacturers must continually churn out products that consumers crave.

The China Study, T. Colin Campbell – detailed connection between nutrition and heart disease, diabetes, and cancer. Examines the source of nutritional confusion produced by powerful lobbies, government entities, and opportunistic scientists. The New York Times has recognized the study as the "Grand Prix of epidemiology" and the most comprehensive large study ever undertaken of the relationship between diet and the risk of developing diseases. It cuts through the haze of misinformation and delivers an insightful message to anyone living with cancer, diabetes, heart disease, obesity, and those concerned with the effects of aging.

The Daniel Plan, Dr. Mark Hyman – This plan focuses on an overall wellness plan for weight loss, mental, and physical health. Created by medical, fitness, and spiritual gurus that include Dr. Oz and Christian pastor. With an emphasis on five key areas of fitness, faith, food, focus, and friends.

The Food Revolution, John Robbins – Heir to the Baskin-Robbins ice cream fortune but turned down to become a vegan activist. His arguments for a plant-based diet are compelling and backed by over 20 years of sustainable agriculture and conscious eating. Insights into America's harmful eating habits give a powerful wake-up call. Shining a light on food politics, our dependence on animal products, provoking awareness, and promoting change.

The Food Babe Way, Vani Hari – Sheds light on the truly shameful and despicable practices employed by the food industry in our country. If there were ever a book that can single-handedly improve the health of our fellow Americans and create meaningful change in the way food is produced and consumed, this is it.

The Four Agreements, Don Miquel Ruiz – Reveals the source of self-limiting beliefs that rob us of joy and create needless suffering. Based on ancient Toltec wisdom, The Four Agreements offer a powerful code of conduct that can rapidly transform our lives into a new experience of freedom, true happiness, and love.

This is Your Brain on Food, Uma Naidoo, MD – Cutting-edge research that explains the many ways in which food contributes to mental health and shows how a sound diet can help treat and prevent a wide range of psychological and cognitive health issues—packed with fascinating science, actionable nutrition recommendations, and delicious, brain-healthy recipes.

Under the Influence, James R. Milam, Ph.D. and Katherine Ketcham – A life-saving approach to alcoholism, who and why it strikes, and how to treat the disease. A guide to the myths and realities of alcoholism.

Water Cure, Dr. F. Batmanghelid – Scientific explanations on why water is vital to your well-being. TWC believes promoting water for health, for healing, and for life is an invaluable public health message.

DOCUMENTARIES

Broken – this investigative docuseries shows how negligence and deceit in the production and marketing of popular consumer items can result in dire outcomes—4-part series; Makeup Mayhem, Big Vape, Deadly Dressers, and Recycling Sham.

Fed Up – Expose unearths a dirty secret of the American Food industry; more get sick from what we eat than many realize. Despite the media attention, the public's fascination with appearance, and government policies to combat childhood obesity – generations of American children will now live shorter lives than their parents.

Food, Inc. – the film examines corporate farming in the United States, concluding that agribusiness produces unhealthy food that is environmentally harmful and abusive of both animals and employees.

Forks Over Knives – examines the profound claim that most, if not all, degenerative diseases that afflict us can be controlled or even reversed by rejecting our present menu of animal-based and processed foods.

Hungry for Change – exposes shocking secrets the diet, weight loss, and food industries do not want you to know about; deception designed to keep you coming back for more. Find out what is keeping you from having the body and health you deserve.

Kiss the Ground – a revolutionary group of activists, scientists, farmers, and politicians band together in a global movement of Regenerative Agriculture that could balance our climate, replenish our vast water supplies, and feed the world.

Super-Size Me – while examining the influence of the fast-food industry, Morgan Spurlock personally explores the consequences on his health of a diet of solely McDonald's food for one month. This movie sheds new light on what has become one of our nation's biggest health problems: obesity.

The Game Changers – explosive rise of plant-eating in professional sports. Exposes outdated myths about food that affect human performance and the health of the entire global population.

The Magic Pill – paradigm shift in eating, embracing fat as the primary fuel. Improving the health of people, animals, and our planet.

What the Health – groundbreaking follow-up film from the creators of the award-winning documentary Cowspiracy. The film exposes the collusion and corruption in government and big business, costing us trillions of healthcare dollars and keeping us sick.

PODCASTS

Heal Thyself, Dr. Christian Gonzalez – is a show based on empowerment. Empowerment of you, **the** viewer, such that you can be your highest self on every level. Through knowledge, we will be giving you **the** information you need to make informed decisions. We lead you to the water; you deep dive in.

The Doctor's Farmacy, Mark Hyman MD – deep conversations about critical issues of our time in health, wellness, food, and politics. We see an increased burden of chronic disease, driven by our food and food system and perpetuated by agriculture, food, and health care policies that do not support health. We need to rethink disease and reimagine a food system and health care system that protects health, unburdens the economy from obesity and chronic illness, and protects the environment creating a nation of healthy children and citizens.

WEBSITES AND NEWSLETTERS

Ewg.org, Environmental Health Movement
Health Nut News, Erin Elizabeth
Mercola.com, Dr. Joseph Mercola
The Whole Journey, Christa Orecchio
The Food Babe, Vani Hari
Wellness Mama, Katie Wells

"No disease that can be treated by diet should be treated with any other means."

- MOSES MAIMONIDES

CHAPTER 10: RECIPES

The recipes included in this book have been intentionally chosen to be interchangeable with the ingredients of each season. Swap out different produce selections to enjoy them throughout the year.

Eating seasonally has many benefits:

Taste - In-season produce is often tastier than out-of-season produce because it does not have to be shipped as far (or at all) and can ripen for longer on the plant.

Health - For the same reason that in-season produce tastes better, it is also generally higher in nutrients.

Boosts the economy - you are actively helping your regional farms and businesses and your regional economy. You are also contributing to a healthy job market, supporting local families, and ensuring that your community is supported with services and programs.

More affordable - when choosing to buy from local farms and businesses and eat seasonally, you can generally expect to pay less for quality food and produce. Importing food into the US is incredibly complicated and expensive.

More sustainable for the environment - transporting produce across the globe has a significant impact on the environment than the pick-up truck used to deliver CSA boxes from your local farmer's market. You are more likely to support smaller, organic farms.

What is in season, and when?

Spring: Endive, fennel, spring onions, radishes, lettuce, cauliflower, spinach, pineapple, mushrooms, artichoke, avocado, spring peas, asparagus, beets, strawberries, apricots, brussels sprouts, peas, and kale.

Summer: Garlic, cherries, cucumber, kale, strawberries, cabbage, carrots, onion, leek, peas, zucchini, corn, broccoli, fennel, apricots, blueberries, potatoes, peach, tomatoes, cauliflower, green beans, peppers, cantaloupe, apples, and watermelon.

Fall: Squash, cabbage, tomatoes, pomegranates, pumpkin, grapes, kale, persimmons, pears, peppers, carrots, cabbage, acorn squash, eggplant, cauliflower, apples, broccoli, chard, sweet potatoes, brussels sprouts, and beets.

Winter: Celery root, winter squash, kale, potatoes, lemons, brussels sprouts, leek, oranges, turnips, radishes, cabbage, parsnips, cauliflower, broccoli, oranges, collards, grapefruit, tangerines, rutabagas, and brussels sprouts.

⌣ THE BASICS ⌣

Roasted Vegetables
Makes 3 - 4 cups

Ingredients:
- 1 yellow beet, peeled
- 1 rutabaga, turnip, or parsnip, scrubbed
- 2 large carrots, peeled
- 1 head broccoli or cauliflower, trimmed
- 2 tablespoon coconut or olive oil

Directions:
1. Preheat your oven to 400 degrees. If you have a convection roast option, use it.
2. Cut all the vegetables into bite-sized pieces, aiming for relatively equal sizes.

3. Place veggies in a roasting dish and drizzle with olive oil or coconut oil.

4. Roast for 15-20 minutes, tossing halfway through. You will know your veggies are done when they are fork-tender, meaning you can easily pierce them with a fork.

5. Store extras in a glass container with a tight-fitting lid in the fridge for 5-6 days.

Brown Rice
Makes 3 cups cooked

Ingredients:
- 1 cup brown rice
- 2 cups water

Directions:
1. Put rice and water into a medium-sized pot and bring to a boil over medium-high heat.
2. Reduce heat to medium-low, cover, and simmer until the liquid is completely absorbed and rice is tender for about 40 minutes.
3. When done, let sit for 10 minutes and fluff rice with a fork.

Quinoa
Makes 3 cups cooked

Ingredients:
- 1 cup quinoa
- 2 cups water or broth

Directions:
1. Place quinoa and liquid into a medium-sized pot and bring to a boil over medium-high heat.
2. Reduce heat to low, cover, and simmer until the liquid is completely absorbed about 15-20 minutes.
3. When done, fluff quinoa with a fork. You will know your quinoa is ready when it looks like it has grown little tails – this is the germ separating from the seed.

⌒ BREAKFAST ⌒

My Favorite Smoothie
1 serving

Ingredients:
- 1 medium banana
- 1 cup dark greens – spinach, kale, collards, packed
- ½ cup frozen fruit of your choice
- 1 cup almond milk
- 1 cup coconut water
- 2 scoops protein powder (optional)
- 2 teaspoons flax seed (optional)
- ½ Inch fresh turmeric root (optional)
- 1 teaspoon bee pollen (optional)
- 1 scoop powdered greens (optional)

Directions:
Place all desired ingredients in blender, bullet, ninja; mix on high until well blended. Enjoy!

NOTES: (benefits of above ingredients)
Bee Pollen: high antioxidant, potent fertility improving properties, increases strength, endurance, energy, speed, neutralizes allergies, and helps relieve type 2 diabetes symptoms.

Turmeric; helps alleviate pain and inflammation.

Flaxseed: helps prevent constipation, stabilizes blood sugar, balance hormones, antiviral, antibacterial, and antifungal properties.

Poached Egg with Greens
Serves 1

Ingredients:
- 1-2 free-range organic or farm fresh eggs
- 1 tablespoon white vinegar
- 5 leaves kale, Swiss chard, or collard greens, or two big handfuls of spinach. If using larger leafy greens, remove the hard stems and cut into thin strips.
- 1 clove garlic, finely chopped
- Sea salt and pepper to taste

Directions:
1. Bring a shallow pan of water to a boil. Lower heat and add vinegar. Crack the egg and put in a ladle. Set ladle in water and gently tip eggs out into the simmering water. Cook 5 minutes, then remove eggs with a slotted spoon. Alternately, simply fry an egg in a little butter or olive oil.
2. Meanwhile, heat a skillet with a little olive oil. Add garlic and greens and cook until wilted. You may need to add a splash of water and cover the greens to get them cooked all the way.
3. Plate the greens, top with the egg, and season with a little sea salt and freshly ground pepper.

Nut Butter Overnight Oats

Serves 1

Ingredients:
- ½ cup rolled oats
- 1 tablespoon chia seeds
- ½ cup unsweetened almond or coconut milk
- ½ tablespoon maple syrup
- 2 tablespoon nut butter

Directions:
1. Place the first four ingredients in a mason jar and stir well to combine. Add the nut butter and stir again – do not worry about it being perfectly mixed.
2. Store in the fridge overnight and eat for breakfast the next morning.

Morning Muesli

Serves 1

Ingredients:
- ½ cup rolled oats
- 1-2 tablespoon raw nuts such as walnuts, almonds, or cashews broken into small pieces
- 1 tablespoon unsweetened coconut flakes (optional)
- 1 tablespoon flaxseed meal, preferably freshly ground
- ½ a pear or apple, chopped or ½ cup organic berries
- sprinkle of cinnamon and nutmeg for flavor (optional)
- top with a little coconut or almond milk

Directions:
1. Combine the first 6 ingredients in a bowl. Top with coconut or almond milk and enjoy. You can also pour 4 ounces of boiling water over the top to create a semi-oatmeal type breakfast.

Protein Pancakes
Serves 1

Ingredients:
- 1 small ripe banana
- 1 egg
- 1 tablespoon almond butter
- coconut oil for cooking

Directions:
1. Using a fork, mash banana in a medium-size bowl, add egg and almond butter, and stir until combined.
2. Heat a medium skillet over medium-high heat. When warm, add coconut oil and swirl to coat skillet. When the oil has melted, scoop some of the pancake mix into the pan and cook until set and browned on one side, then flip, cooking and set until browned on the other side, then remove from pan.
3. Serve with a bit of real maple syrup or fresh fruit.

∼ LUNCH ∼

Quinoa Tabbouleh
Serves 4

Ingredients:
- 2 cups broth
- 1 cup quinoa
- 1 cucumber, cut in quarters lengthwise, seeded, and chopped
- 1 cup parsley, rinsed, dried, and finely chopped
- ½ cup cherry or grape tomatoes, quartered
- ¼ cup mint leaves, rinsed, dried, and chopped
- ¼ cup extra virgin olive oil
- ¼ cup lemon juice, freshly squeezed – about 1 lemon
- sea salt and freshly ground pepper to taste

Directions:
1. Place quinoa in a fine-mesh sieve and rinse. Combine broth and quinoa in a pot and bring to a boil. When boiling, cover and reduce heat to low. Allow to simmer for 15 minutes – quinoa is finished when the germ has been expelled from the seed, which will look like grown little tails. Do not stir quinoa (or any grain!) while it is cooking.
2. Combine all ingredients except olive oil and lemon juice in a large bowl and add cooked quinoa.
3. Whisk lemon juice and olive oil until blended, then pour over the quinoa. Toss gently to mix and distribute dressing over the grains and vegetables. Add more lemon juice and olive oil if the salad is too dry.
4. Store in a glass container in the fridge for 4-5 days. A great grab-and-go lunch option.

Chopped Detox Salad
Serves 1

Ingredients:
- 1 boneless, skinless chicken breast
- 1 small handful of cauliflower florets, chopped into small pieces
- ½ bunch kale, de-stemmed and thinly sliced
- 1 carrot, peeled and grated
- Small handful cilantro, washed and finely chopped (optional)
- 1 tablespoon sunflower seeds (optional)

Dressing:
- ½ avocado, peel, and seed removed
- ⅓ cup raw apple cider vinegar
- juice from 1 lemon
- ½ tablespoon fresh cilantro, finely chopped
- 1 teaspoon sea salt
- 1 teaspoon freshly ground pepper

Directions:
1. Bring a medium-size pot of water to a boil and add chicken breast. Turn down the heat and simmer for 15 minutes, or until chicken breast is cooked through and a meat thermometer reads 160 degrees. Drain, let cool, then shred into small pieces.
2. Meanwhile, heat oven to 400 degrees. Place cauliflower and carrot on a baking sheet and drizzle with 1 TB olive oil.
3. Place cooled chicken, cauliflower, kale, carrot, cilantro, and sunflower seeds into a large bowl and toss to combine.
4. Place dressing ingredients in a blender and blend until smooth. Pour dressing over salad and toss to combine, then serve immediately.

Note: Make this dish vegetarian by skipping the chicken and replacing it with 1 C cooked chickpeas, kidney beans, or white beans.

Dill Salmon Salad
Serves 1

Ingredients:
- 1 (6-oz) can wild salmon, drained, or 6-oz cooked wild salmon
- ½ tablespoon capers, drained
- 1 tablespoon finely chopped red onion
- 2 tablespoons hummus
- 1 tablespoon olive oil
- 2 tablespoons rice wine vinegar
- 1 tablespoon fresh dill, chopped, or 1-2 tsp dried dill
- 3 cup salad greens, rinsed and dried
- 2 tablespoons raw sauerkraut (optional)
- sea salt and freshly ground pepper

Directions:
1. Combine the first 7 ingredients in a large bowl and mix well.
2. Add salad greens, and toss to combine until the greens are coated with the salmon mixture.
3. Season with sea salt and freshly ground pepper, taste, and season more if needed. Top with raw sauerkraut if using and enjoy.

Mediterranean Chickpea Salad
Makes 2 servings

Ingredients:
- 1 (14-oz) can chickpeas/garbanzo beans, drained and rinsed
- ½ cup cucumber, chopped
- ½ cup cherry tomatoes, chopped
- ½ cup yellow bell pepper, chopped
- ¼ cup kalamata olives, pitted and chopped
- 1 tablespoon fresh oregano, chopped, or 1 tsp dried
- 1 tablespoon fresh dill, chopped, or 1 tsp dried
- 1 tablespoon red wine vinegar
- 2 teaspoon dijon mustard
- 1 tablespoon olive oil
- 1 teaspoon sea salt
- 1 teaspoon freshly ground pepper
- 3 cup salad greens, washed and dried

Directions:
1. In a small bowl, whisk together the red wine vinegar, Dijon mustard, olive oil, herbs, sea salt, and pepper to make the dressing.
2. Place the salad greens in a large bowl and top with chickpeas/garbanzo beans and chopped vegetables. Drizzle the dressing over the top of the salad, taste, and add more seasoning if needed before serving.

Simple Minestrone
Makes 3-4 servings

Ingredients:
- 1 pound mild Italian chicken sausage
- 1 tablespoon extra-virgin olive oil
- 1 small yellow onion, diced
- 2 garlic cloves, minced
- 4 cups vegetable or chicken broth
- 1 (14-oz) can kidney beans, rinsed and drained
- 1 (14-oz) can diced roasted tomatoes
- 1 bunch kale, washed, de-stemmed and cut into thin ribbons
- 1 teaspoon dried thyme
- sea salt and pepper to taste

Directions:
1. In a large pot, sauté chicken sausage for 3-4 minutes, using a wooden spoon to break it into small pieces. Add olive oil, onion, and garlic, and sauté for 5 minutes more, stirring occasionally.
2. Add broth and tomatoes, then cover and bring to a simmer, cooking for 20 minutes. Stir in kidney beans, kale, and dried thyme and simmer for 5 minutes more, then serve.

⟶ DINNER ⟵

Chicken Sausage, Kale and White Beans
Serves 2

Ingredients:
- 1 tablespoon olive oil
- 1 large bunch kale, washed, de-stemmed, and roughly chopped
- 4 garlic cloves, chopped
- 1 pound chicken sausage, removed from casing
- 1 (14-oz) can cannellini beans (or white kidney beans), rinsed and drained
- salt, pepper, and white wine vinegar (optional)

Directions:
1. Heat a large skillet over medium-high and add olive oil.
2. Add chicken sausage and break up using a spatula. Sauté until lightly browned, about 5 minutes.
3. Add garlic cloves and beans and cook 2 additional minutes.
4. Add kale, toss to combine, and cover the pan for 1-2 minutes. Ready to serve when kale leaves are wilted but not mushy.
5. Add salt and pepper to taste and a splash of white wine vinegar if desired.

Asian Steamed Cod with Bok Choy
Serves 2

Ingredients:
- 2 six-oz skinless, wild-caught cod fillets
- 3 tablespoons rice vinegar
- 2 tablespoons wheat-free tamari or soy sauce
- 6 baby bok choy, washed and sliced in quarters lengthwise
- 1-2 tablespoons grated peeled fresh ginger
- 4 scallions, cut in thirds and thinly sliced lengthwise

Directions:
1. In a small skillet, combine rice vinegar, wheat-free tamari, and ginger. Add fish to the skillet, bring to a boil; reduce heat to a simmer, and cover and cook for 5 minutes.
2. Add baby bok choy and scallions on top of the fish, and replace the lid for 1-2 more minutes until scallions and bok choy have wilted and the fish is opaque and flakes easily.
3. Serve with a side of brown rice or quinoa if you would like a heartier meal.

Tuscan Vegetable Stew
Makes 6 servings

Ingredients:
- 1 tablespoon olive oil
- ½ yellow onion, chopped
- 1 zucchini, cut in half lengthwise, and sliced
- 1 yellow squash, cut in half lengthwise, and sliced
- 4 oz cremini mushrooms, wiped clean, the tip of foot cut off and cut in quarters
- 3 garlic cloves, minced
- 1 jar or can diced tomatoes, with their juices
- 4-6 cups organic vegetable or chicken broth
- 1 small bunch of escarole or lacinato kale, washed, dried, and cut into thin strips
- 1 sprig fresh oregano or 1 tsp dried
- 2 (14-oz) cans white kidney beans/navy beans/cannellini beans, rinsed and drained
- freshly ground pepper

Directions:
1. Heat a large pot to medium-high. Add olive oil and onion and cook until onion is fragrant; 4-5 minutes.
2. Add zucchini, yellow squash, and mushrooms, and sauté for 10 minutes. Add garlic cloves and stir for about a minute.
3. Add tomatoes, broth, and oregano. Bring to a low boil, reduce heat, and then simmer for 15 minutes. Gently stir the beans and escarole/kale into soup and cook for another 5 minutes or until beans are heated through, and greens are wilted. Serve with freshly ground pepper on top.

Korean Rice Bowl
Makes 2 servings

Ingredients:
- 1 tablespoon olive or coconut oil
- 1 small yellow onion, chopped
- 1 pound ground free-range organic turkey or chicken
- 3 garlic cloves, minced
- 4 oz shiitake mushrooms, tough foot removed and sliced thinly
- 2 carrots, scrubbed and grated
- ½ small head of red cabbage, finely chopped
- 3 tablespoons wheat-free tamari sauce or coconut aminos
- 1 tablespoon rice wine vinegar
- ½ tablespoon fish sauce
- red pepper flakes (optional)

Directions:
1. In a large skillet or wok, heat olive or coconut oil over medium-high heat. Add onion and ground meat, and sauté for 5 minutes, stirring frequently.
2. Add garlic, shiitakes, carrots, and cabbage, and toss to combine. Continue cooking for another 5-10 minutes or until meat is cooked through and vegetables are cooked.
3. Whisk together wheat-free tamari, rice wine vinegar, and fish sauce together in a small bowl, then pour over the ground meat and vegetable mix. Stir to combine, then serve.
4. Serve with cooked brown rice.

Southwestern Rice and Bean Bowls
Serves 2

Ingredients:
- 2 cups cooked brown rice
- 1 tablespoon olive oil
- ¼ small yellow onion, diced
- 2 garlic cloves, diced
- ½ jalapeno, diced
- 1 zucchini, quartered lengthwise and sliced
- 1 teaspoon dried oregano
- 1 teaspoon cumin
- dash of cayenne pepper (optional)
- 1 (14-oz) can pinto beans, rinsed and drained
- 1-2 teaspoons raw apple cider vinegar or rice wine vinegar
- Optional: toppings: salsa, chopped cilantro, diced avocado, hot sauce, chopped green onion, or sliced radishes

Directions:
1. Re-heat brown rice in a small saucepan set on medium-low with 1-2 TB water.
2. Heat a large skillet over medium heat and add onion, garlic, jalapeno, and zucchini. Cook until veggies are starting to brown. Add oregano, cumin, and cayenne pepper and stir to incorporate.
3. Add pinto beans and cook until they are heated thoroughly; about 5 minutes. Top with a few sprinkles of apple cider vinegar.
4. Place re-heated brown rice and bean mixture into a bowl. Top with whatever your heart desires. My favorites are salsa, diced avocado, sliced radishes, and chopped green onion.

Rainbow Stir-Fry
Serves 2

Ingredients:
- 1 teaspoon olive, avocado, or coconut oil
- 3 green onions, trimmed and cut into 1-inch slices
- 3 garlic cloves, minced
- 6 oz shiitake mushrooms, tip of foot removed and sliced thinly
- 2 carrots, scrubbed and cut thinly on the angle
- 1 red bell pepper, seeded, cored, and cut into bite-sized strips
- 3 bunches baby bok choy, cut into thin strips
- 3 tablespoons wheat-free tamari sauce (gluten-free soy sauce)
- 1 tablespoon rice vinegar
- ½ tablespoon grated ginger (optional)
- red pepper flakes (optional)
- cooked brown rice (for serving, see page 4 for instructions)

Directions:
1. In a large skillet, heat oil and add onion. Sauté for a few minutes, then add shiitake mushrooms, carrots, and bell pepper. Stir-fry for 4-5 minutes, adding water to the pan by the tablespoon if the veggies start to stick.
2. Next, add bok choy, garlic, tamari sauce, and rice wine vinegar. Grate ginger over the top if using. Toss to combine and continue tossing until bok choy has wilted. Turn off heat, sprinkle red pepper flakes over the veggies, and serve over brown rice.
3. Season with more wheat-free tamari sauce or rice vinegar as needed.

⁓ SALADS AND SIDES ⁓

Asian Broccoli Salad
Servings: 4 - 6

Ingredients:
- 1 large head broccoli, cut into florets
- 2 scallions, chopped
- ½ red onion, sliced
- ¼ cup chopped cashews or sliced almonds
- 2 tablespoons sesame seeds

Dressing:
- ¼ cup almond or peanut butter
- 1 teaspoon grated ginger
- 2 tablespoons low sodium tamari or soy sauce
- 1 tablespoon rice wine vinegar
- 1 teaspoon raw honey
- pinch of sesame oil
- 3-4 tablespoons hot water, more as needed
- sea salt and pepper, to taste

Directions:
- Bring a pot of water to boil. Add broccoli and cook for 1-2 minutes. Drain under cold water—place in a bowl with the remaining salad ingredients.
- To make dressing, place all the ingredients in a bowl and whisk until well combined. Pour dressing over broccoli and toss to combine.

Asparagus and Green Bean Salad

Servings: 6 – 8

Ingredients:
Salad

- 1-pound french beans, stems removed
- 2 pounds fresh asparagus, woody ends trimmed
- 1 tablespoon finely chopped shallot
- 1 tablespoon finely chopped fresh chives
- 5 slices bacon, cooked and chopped
- 3 hard-cooked eggs, peeled and cut into quarter

Vinaigrette

- 2 teaspoon Dijon mustard
- 3-4 teaspoons balsamic vinegar
- 3 tablespoons olive oil
- salt and pepper to taste

Directions:

- Fill a large pot with water. Bring to boil and add beans and asparagus. Return to boil, lower heat, and simmer about 2-4 minutes until vegetables are tender but crisp. (Blanching)
- Drain and refresh under cold water. Let cool completely.
- In a small bowl, whisk together mustard, balsamic vinegar, and olive oil until smooth. Season to taste. Set aside.
- Chop cooled vegetables and transfer them to a salad bowl. Sprinkle with shallot, chives, and bacon.
- Drizzle with vinaigrette and top with eggs.

Kale Salad
Yield: 3-4 servings

Ingredients:
- 1 large bunch raw kale
- 1/4 cup sliced raw almonds
- 1/2 cup cherry tomatoes, cut in half
- 1/2 lemon, juiced
- 1/4 cup extra virgin olive oil
- pecorino cheese, shaved (optional)
- sea salt and ground black pepper to taste

Directions:
- Remove stems and chop kale into thin ribbons.
- Massage with lemon juice to soften the leaves and cut the bitterness.
- Combine in a large bowl with olive oil and lemon juice.
- Massage until kale softens and drain any liquid released from the kale.
- Toast almonds in a skillet over medium heat until they begin to brown. Remove from heat.
- Add the almonds and tomatoes to the kale and toss.
- Season with sea salt and freshly ground black pepper.
- Top salad with shaved pecorino cheese (optional

Mix it up by adding or swapping out different nuts, fruits, and vegetables. This salad holds up well to make ahead and eat for lunches throughout the week.

Citrus Beet Salad
Yield: 4 -6 servings

Ingredients:
- 3-4 medium beets
- 2-3 tangerines – peeled, seeded, and sectioned
- ¼ cup chopped walnuts or pecans
- 2 tablespoons oil – olive, walnut, or avocado
- sea salt and pepper to taste
- 2 tablespoons citrus vinegar or other flavored vinegar

Directions:
- Boiling: Clean, quarter, then boil beets until tender when a fork is inserted. Drain and cool. Peel beets, cut into smaller pieces and add in remaining ingredients, stir, and serve.
- Roasting: Clean, peel, cut into quarter-size chunks. Lightly coat with olive oil. Roast in oven at 400 degrees for 15 minutes. Cool. Add in tangerine pieces, chopped nuts if desired, drizzle with oil and vinegar. Lightly season.

Note: Boiling with beet skin retains a higher nutrient value.

Moroccan Carrot Salad

Yield: Serves 4-6

Eating lots of naturally sweet vegetables helps reduce sugar cravings.

Ingredients:

- 6 medium carrots
- ½ medium onion
- 1 large lemon or 2 tablespoons juice
- 3 tablespoons olive oil
- ½ teaspoon sea salt
- ¼ teaspoon black pepper
- ¼ cup raisins

Optional Ingredients:

- 1 teaspoon curry powder, turmeric, cinnamon
- ¼ cup chopped almonds (or another nut choice)

Directions:

- Rinse carrots and shred them with a grater or food processor.
- Dice onion and combine with carrots.
- Add remaining ingredients and stir well.

～ DRESSINGS ～

Ranch

Ingredients:
- ½ cup Plain full-fat or Greek yogurt
- 1 teaspoon dried dill weed
- 1 clove garlic, minced
- ½ teaspoon sea salt
- ½ teaspoon black pepper
- 6 tablespoons olive oil
- 2 tablespoons parmesan (optional)

Directions:
- Put all ingredients except oil in blender or food processor, blend until smooth.
- Very slowly, add the oil so that it emulsifies.
- Use immediately, or store in a covered container in the fridge for up to ten days.

Variations:
- Use 2 teaspoons of herbs like dill, mint, or basil.
- Use avocado instead of yogurt.

Store-bought versions often contain unhealthy ingredients such as vegetable oils, sugar, soy, xanthan gum, modified food starch, artificial flavors, calcium disodium (preservative), MSG. Easy enough to make your own, store in refrigeration in an airtight container.

French Vinaigrette

Ingredients:
- 4-6 cloves garlic, chopped
- 1 tablespoon Dijon mustard
- 1 large handful parsley, washed, dried, and roughly chopped
- ⅔ cup rice wine vinegar
- ⅓ cup extra virgin olive oil
- salt and pepper to taste

Directions:
1. Place all ingredients in a glass jar with a tight-fitting lid and shake vigorously until ingredients are thoroughly mixed. Taste and adjust the seasonings to your personal preference.
2. Store in the fridge for about a week, shaking again before each use.

Garlic Tahini Dressing
Makes 1 Cup

Ingredients:
- 3 tablespoons tahini
- 2 large cloves garlic
- 2 tablespoons maple syrup
- Juice of a lemon
- 1 teaspoon red pepper flakes (optional)
- hot water

Directions:
1. Combine all ingredients in a bowl and whisk together.
2. Slowly add hot water, 1-2 TB at a time, while whisking the dressing until thinned.
3. Store this dressing in the fridge for 3 days, whisking again before serving, adding more water if need.

Avocado Dressing

Ingredients:
- 1 ripe avocado, pitted and cut into chunks
- 1 clove garlic
- ½ tablespoon fresh lemon juice
- 3 tablespoons olive oil
- ½ teaspoon sea salt
- dash cayenne pepper (optional, but it gives this dressing a fun kick)
- 1-2 tablespoons water

Directions:
1. Combine all ingredients in a blender, then blend until smooth. Taste, then add more water by the tablespoon until you reach your desired consistency.
2. This dressing will store in the refrigerator for 1-2 days, but it is so yummy you probably will not have much left.

Cilantro Lime Dressing

Ingredients:
- ½ bunch cilantro, washed well and dried
- 4 tablespoons olive oil
- juice of a lime
- 1 tablespoon rice wine vinegar
- 1 teaspoon honey or maple syrup (optional)
- ½ teaspoon sea salt

Directions:
1. Place all ingredients in a blender and blend until smooth.
2. This dressing stores well in the fridge for about a week in an airtight container. Be sure to shake well before using.

∼ SNACKS ∼

Chia Seed Pudding
Makes 1 – 2 servings

Ingredients:
- 1 cup milk, or milk alternative
- 4 tablespoons chia seeds
- ½ ripe banana
- 2 pitted dates or 2 teaspoons raw honey / maple syrup
- OPTIONAL: 1 tablespoon raw cacao
- OPTIONAL: Top with fresh fruit

Directions:
1. Put all ingredients in a food processor, pulse until blended
2. Pour into an airtight container.
3. Refrigerate 1-2 hours, or overnight.

If you do not have a food processor, use a jar with a lid:
- mash banana
- OMIT dates; use honey or maple syrup, if desired
- Add chia seeds and milk; shake well.
- Refrigerate 1-2 hours or overnight.

Kale Chips

Ingredients:
- 1 bunch lacinato or red Russian kale, rinsed and dried
- olive oil
- sea salt

Directions:
1. Heat oven to 350-375 degrees, depending on your range. The kale chips burn quickly, so keep the temperature on the lower end, especially if your oven tends to get hot or has hot spots.
2. Clean kale and remove the thick stem by folding each leaf in half lengthwise and cutting it away. Make sure kale is quite dry.
3. Pour a little olive oil into a dipping bowl. Dip your fingers in the olive oil and rub over each kale leaf, front, and back.
4. Arrange kale on several baking sheets, making sure not to crowd the leaves. Sprinkle sea salt over the top.
5. Bake for 3-5 minutes, keeping an eye on the chips to make sure they do not burn. Turn the chips over and then bake for another 2-3 minutes. You may need more or less time depending on your oven. When they are bright green, the chips are ready – discard any brown leaves as they are burnt and quite bitter.
6. Spice it up by sprinkling smoked paprika, cumin, or curry on before baking.

Spicy Chickpeas

Ingredients:

- 2 (15-oz) cans chickpeas/garbanzo beans, rinsed and drained
- 2 tablespoons olive oil
- 1 teaspoon smoked or regular paprika
- pinch cayenne pepper
- 1 teaspoon sea salt

Directions:

1. Preheat oven to 400 degrees.
2. In a large bowl, whisk together the olive oil, paprika, cayenne, and sea salt. Add chickpeas and toss until evenly coated.
3. Spread chickpeas in a single layer on a baking sheet and bake for 30-35 minutes or until golden brown and crispy. Halfway through baking, shake the tray to toss the chickpeas.
4. Remove from oven and let cool, then serve. Store in an airtight container on the counter for up to 3 days.

Turmeric Hummus
Makes 6 servings

Ingredients:
- 1 (14-oz) can chickpeas (garbanzo beans), rinsed and drained
- 2 garlic cloves
- 2 tablespoons tahini
- 2 tablespoons olive oil
- 2 teaspoons turmeric powder
- 1 teaspoon sea salt
- pinch cayenne pepper

Directions:
1. Combine all ingredients in a food processor or blender, and pulse until smooth.
2. Check the texture as you go; you may need to add more olive oil by the tablespoon to get your desired consistency. Taste and adjust seasonings to your liking, then serve.

Homemade Trail Mix

Ingredients:
- ½ cup macadamia nuts
- ½ cup raw walnuts
- ½ cup raw pumpkin seeds
- ½ cup raw sunflower seeds
- ½ cup goji berries, dried cranberries, or dried currants (watch sugar added content)
- ¼ cup golden raisins

Directions:
1. Mix and store in an airtight container.
2. Pre-portion this into ½ C servings, so you do not eat the whole batch at once.

Additional Snack Ideas:
- Hummus or black bean dip with cut vegetables
- A small handful of nuts
- 2 slices turkey breast
- A small handful of mixed fresh olives
- One or two hardboiled eggs
- Raw sauerkraut
- Sliced apple with 1-2 TB nut butter (peanut, almond, cashew, macadamia, or even sunflower seed)
- A small salad with lots of crunchy veggies and sunflower seeds
- Half an avocado
- Homemade trail mix
- Steamed artichokes with tahini for dipping
- Roasted pumpkin seeds
- Coconut date rolls
- Fruit smoothies with a handful of leafy greens like spinach or collard greens
- Green juices
- Lara bars are made from just fruit and nuts and are found in many grocery and convenience stores.

∼ SWEET TREATS ∼

Raw Chocolate Pudding
Makes 4 ramekins of pudding

Ingredients:
- 1 small or ½ large ripe avocado
- 1 very ripe banana
- ½ can coconut milk
- 2 tablespoons raw cacao powder
- 1 tablespoon raw honey

Directions:
1. Add ingredients to a bowl, blender, or food processor. Blend until smooth, adjusting the amount of coconut milk if needed to get a nice creamy consistency similar to real pudding.
2. Divide into 4 small bowls or ramekins, chill for 30 minutes and enjoy! The raw chocolate pudding will keep in the fridge for few days when covered.

Cashew Energy Bites
Yield: 24

These cashew energy bites are similar to Lara Bars Cashew bar, with added pea protein, maca, and raw honey for additional raw energy and superfood nutrition. Remember, just because they are a healthier version of a treat, they are still treats.

Ingredients:
- 1 cup pitted dates
- 1 ½ cups raw cashews
- 2 teaspoons maca powder
- ¼ cup pea protein powder
- 1 tablespoon raw honey
- ¼ teaspoon sea salt
- ¼ cup sesame or other seeds

Directions:
1. Add dates, cashews, maca, protein powder in a food processor, pulse until combined
2. Add vanilla, honey, salt, pulsing until the mixture forms a ball
3. Place seeds in a shallow bowl. Make one inch balls with the mixture, roll in hemp seeds to coat

Make a batch of these sweet treats and keep a couple on hand throughout your day to combat energy dip. They will stay good in an airtight container for 5-7 days. Make a double batch and put some in the freezer. These can be made in a food chopper or food processor(preferred).

Maca benefits from chronic fatigue syndrome, enhance energy, stamina, athletic performance, hormones, and memory. Seeds contain essential healthy fats and proteins to maintain overall health.

Black Bean Brownies

Ingredients:
- 1/2 cup cacao (cocoa) powder unsweetened
- 1 can chickpeas, drained and rinsed
- 1 can black beans, drained and rinsed
- 4 eggs
- 2/3 cup agave nectar or honey
- 1/2 teaspoon baking powder
- 1 cup dark chocolate chips
- ¼ cup chopped walnuts (Optional)
- shredded coconut (Optional)

Directions:
1. In a blender or food processor, combine beans and eggs.
2. Add sweetener, baking powder, and cacao, process until smooth.
3. Stir in chocolate chips and nuts into batter
4. Pour batter into a 9-inch nonstick pan at 350 degrees for 45 min; or into 48 lined mini cupcake trays and bake for 18 minutes.
5. Sprinkle with coconut, choc chips, and walnuts
6. Allow to cool, cut, and serve.

These are surprisingly delicious, and nobody will guess that they are made from beans!

Peanut Butter Cookie Dough Bites
Makes 12-16

Ingredients:
- 2/3 cup creamy peanut butter
- ½ protein powder
- ¼ cup honey
- 1/3 cup unsweetened shredded coconut
- 1/3 cup dark chocolate chips

Directions:
1. In a large bowl, mix peanut butter and honey.
2. Stir in protein powder and coconut until combined, then fold in chocolate chips.
3. Roll into 1 or 2 inch balls, place on wax paper-lined pan.
4. Refrigerate for at least 30 minutes.

Baked Apples or Pears

Cut in half and core an apple or pear—place in a baking dish with a tablespoon of butter. Sprinkle cinnamon and nutmeg over the fruit—Bake in a 350-degree oven for about 30 minutes, or until the fruit is tender.

"Oatmeal" Raisin Cookies
Yield: Makes 24

Gluten and grain-free, SCD (Specific Carbohydrate Diet) Approved

Ingredients:
- 1 cup smooth almond butter
- 1 egg
- 1/3 cup honey
- 2 teaspoons vanilla extract
- ½ cup unsweetened shredded coconut
- 2 teaspoons ground cinnamon
- ½ teaspoon baking soda
- ½ teaspoon salt
- ¾ cup raisins

Directions:
1. Preheat oven 350. Use nonstick silicone mats or parchment paper-lined cookie sheets.
2. Blend almond butter, egg, honey, and vanilla until creamy.
3. Combine dry ingredients in a separate bowl and blend
4. Add to wet ingredients. Mix well.
5. Spoon 1 tablespoon batter per cookie onto baking sheets, spaced about 1 inch
6. Bake for 10-12 min. They will appear a little wet out of the oven. Let cool completely.

~ DRINKS ~

Hot Chocolate Elixir
Serves 1

Ingredients:
- 1 tablespoon raw cacao powder
- ¼ teaspoon cinnamon
- dash cayenne pepper
- 2-4 oz full-fat coconut milk
- squeeze of honey (if needed)

Directions:
1. Put first 4 ingredients in a large mug and pour 8-10 ounces of hot water over the top. Whisk until well combined and frothy.
2. Add coconut milk and squeeze of honey if needed. Drink up!

Ginger Honey Switchel
2 - 4 servings

A fermented drink that combines the benefits of apple cider vinegar, raw honey (or molasses), and ginger for a refreshing and electrolyte drink. Neutralizing the body's PH balance from acidic to more alkaline and aiding in digestion and sugar cravings.

Ingredients:
- 2 tablespoons unfiltered apple cider vinegar
- 3 tablespoons raw honey or blackstrap molasses
- 2-inch piece fresh ginger root, peeled and finely minced
- 4 cups water
- ½ of fresh lime, juiced and zested

Directions:
- Mix all ingredients in a large jar, cover, and shake well
- Place in the refrigerator overnight
- To serve, pour over ice or add seltzer water if desired.

Note: If using seltzer water, only add half the amount of listed water to the jar. Then, add the other half of seltzer water when serving.

Tea Mocha or Latte
Serves 1

Dandy blends are a blend of dandelion, chicory root, beets, barley, and rye. It contains no gluten or caffeine and a great replacement for coffee in taste, lacking bitterness, and acidity, with a host of health benefits. Helpful for digestion, kidney, and liver support, loaded with antioxidants, regulates blood sugar levels, cancer-fighting agents, blood pressure stabilizer, immune aid, and inflammation reducer.

Ingredients:
- ¾ cup unsweetened almond milk, hot
- ¾ cup boiling water
- 2 tablespoons Dandy blends instant tea mix

Optional Ingredients:
- 1 – 2 teaspoons honey
- 2 tablespoons unsweetened cacao powder (to make it a mocha)

Directions:
1. Warm milk, then mix in Dandy Blends tea, honey, and cacao if making mocha.
2. Add hot water and stir well. Enjoy!

Turmeric Golden Milk
Serves 2

This drink is not only delicious, but it also helps improve immunity, soothes a sore throat and cough, reduces inflammation, detoxing the liver, and so much more.

Ingredients:
- 2 cups coconut milk, or milk of your choice
- ½ teaspoon turmeric powder
- pinch of black pepper (for maximum absorption of active curcumin in turmeric)
- 1 teaspoon cinnamon

Optional Ingredients:
- 1/8 teaspoon ground ginger
- 1/8 teaspoon ground cloves
- 1/8 teaspoon ground nutmeg
- 1-2 teaspoons raw honey or maple syrup

Directions:
1. Warm milk in a small saucepan over low heat, 8 -10 minutes.
2. Mix in spices and stir well.
3. Serve and enjoy!

*"God, grant me the Serenity to accept
the things I cannot change,
the Courage to change the things I can,
and the Wisdom to know the difference."*
- REINHOLD NIEBUHR

THE TWELVE STEPS OF
ALCOHOLICS ANONYMOUS

1. We admitted we were powerless over alcohol – that our lives had become unmanageable.

2. Came to believe that a Power greater than ourselves could restore us to sanity.

3. Made a decision to turn our will and our lives over to the care of God as we understood him.

4. Made a searching and fearless moral inventory of ourselves.

5. Admitted to God, to ourselves, and to another human being the exact nature of our wrongs.

6. Were entirely ready to have God remove all these defects of character.

7. Humbly asked Him to remove our shortcomings.

8. Made a list of all the persons we had harmed and became willing to make amends to them all.

9. Made direct amends to such people whenever possible, except when to do so would injure them or others.

10. Continued to take personal inventory and when we were wrong promptly admitted it.

11. Sought through prayer and meditation to improve our conscious contact with God *as we understood Him*, praying only for knowledge of His will for us and the power to carry that out.

12. Having a spiritual awakening as a result of these steps, we tried to carry this message to alcoholics, and to practice these principles in all of our affairs.

The Twelve Steps are taken from *Alcoholics Anonymous*, 4th ed. (New York: Alcoholics Anonymous World Services, 2001), 59 – 60. In the same book, the *Doctor's Opinion* and the first seven chapters provide the complete directions for the Steps as described here.